OTHER
BOOKS BY
ADELINE FOO

Ben's Friends from the Rainforest

Secret Hoarder

LOST IN THE SECRET GARDEN

THE MIDNIGHT TREE

THE BEADED SLIPPERS

THE
AMULET

THE KITCHEN GOD

Chilli Padi

monsters on the wall

THE THING UNDER MY BED

GUAI WU
THE MONSTER CHILD

NU NU THE RING-NECKED MONSTER

THE DIARY OF AMOS LEE

I Sit, I Write, I Flush!

Written by
ADELINE FOO

Illustrated by
STEPHANIE WONG

EPIGRAM

FIFTH PRINTING, 2010
Text © Adeline Foo 2009
Illustrations © Epigram 2009

PUBLISHED BY EPIGRAM
1008 Toa Payoh North #03-08 Singapore 318996
Tel: (65) 6292 4456 / Fax: (65) 6292 4414
enquiry@epigram.com.sg / www.epigram.com.sg

DISTRIBUTED BY
Market Asia Distributors
601 Sims Drive #04-05
Pan-I Complex, Singapore 387382
Tel: (65) 6744 8483, 6744 8486
jl@marketasia.com.sg

ILLUSTRATIONS AND COVER DESIGN BY
Stephanie Wong

EDITED BY
Ruth Wan

NATIONAL LIBRARY BOARD SINGAPORE
CATALOGUING IN PUBLICATION DATA
Foo, Adeline, 1971-
The Diary of Amos Lee: I Sit, I Write, I Flush / written by Adeline Foo,
illustrated by Stephanie Wong. – Singapore: Epigram, 2009.
p. cm.
ISBN-13: 978-981-08-2484-6 (pbk.)

1. Boys – Singapore – Juvenile fiction. 2. Children – Singapore – Juvenile fiction.
3. Singapore – Juvenile fiction. I. Wong, Stephanie, 1979- II. Title.

PZ7
428.6 -- dc22   OCN315940572

Printed in Singapore.

This diary began as Mum's New Year resolution to get me to write.

She came up with this weird idea that we should make good use of our time in the bathroom. On a wall above the toilet seat, she put in a wire rack to hold an old jotter book, some pens and coloured pencils. She said that when I am doing my big business, I can write. "Five to eight minutes max!" she said. "I don't want you to develop piles!"

I think that means something that blocks my poop from coming out.

"And why must I do this?" I asked.

"It's either this or you spend one hour every day writing one composition!" she said.

"Who wouldn't pick writing in the bathroom?" I thought to myself.

And so my writing in the bathroom began.

Dad said it would teach me to multi-task, a very important skill to have when I go out to work next time.

My entries started with the boring old stuff – describing my family, my day at school, things I would love to do to my pesky little sister, and so on... then Mum got this new job as a writer for a magazine.

She received the weirdest of assignments and would drag my sister and I along to check out new places. And that's how I got more things to write about. Some of these places Mum brought us were quite fun. I started collecting entry tickets to these places, so that I could enter my name in the Guinness World Records one day. That way, I will become famous, and one day, my diary will be worth a lot of money!

MY FAMILY

ABOUT ME
- HOW I GOT MY NAME!

Mum had weird food cravings when she was pregnant with me. At one time, it was for char siew bao. Another time, it was for cookies - double chocolate macadamia nut. She ate so many cookies in the nine months carrying me that when the doctor asked what she was naming her baby boy as I was being pushed out of her womb, she shouted, "He will be famous one day. I will call him Amos!"

And that's how I got my name - Amos Lee. Well, it could have been worse. Imagine being called Lee Char Siew!

MY DAD

Dad works at the airport. He says it's an important job. He has to make sure that the airport is running 24 hours a day and that nothing breaks down, so that he doesn't get complaints.

MY MUM

I was happier when Mum had a job. But she quit to spend more time with my sister and I. She drives us to school, cooks, cleans the house, irons our clothes, sends us for tuition, swimming and ballet classes. She is very busy but she knows when I am going to the bathroom. "Write in the bathroom!" she yells all the time. I wish she had a real job.

MY SISTER

Just turned five. I call her WPI. Whiny. Pesky. Irritating.

AH KONG AND PO-PO

Ah Kong and Po-Po have taken care of us since we were babies. Since Mum is home now, they only come over a few times a week. Po-Po cooks dinner and Ah Kong watches us when Mum has to leave the house for errands or to meet her friends. Most nights when Ah Kong and Po-Po are late in getting home, they just stay over at our house.

MUM FOUND A JOB!

Mum was very excited today. She was asked by an old boss to work as a writer. She can write from home (not very good news for me) but some days, she won't be home as she has to go for meetings. That's the good part.

9pm

I heard Mum telling Dad that maybe she could bring WPI and I along for her ~~ass-in-mens~~ Oh man...
                              (assignments!)
See, now I know Mum reads my diary. She cannot stand it when I do not spell correctly.

Saturday, 5 January

MUM'S 1ST ASSIGNMENT — BREAKFAST WATCH

Mum said she needed to observe what locals eat for breakfast. I was excited as, well, I love eating! Mum's editor said that the article must cover "traditional breakfast favourites". Sounds interesting enough.

I only know of McDonald's hot cakes, fried carrot cake – must be black, and kaya toast. We usually eat these. But Mum said her article has to be more balanced, including choices of food eaten by all races.

"Right, what about McDonald's Big Breakfast, fried carrot cake – can be white, and kaya bun?" I asked.

Nope, fried carrot cake didn't meet her cryteeria. Mum said *It's 'criteria', Amos!*
she would bring me along for 'food tasting' at coffee shops
and hawker centres. Yippee! This is one assignment I don't
mind helping out with!

Sunday, 6 January

BREAKFAST AT CHIN MEE CHIN

Our first stop – a coffee shop along East Coast Road.
Been around since 1925, Mum said. Mosaic tiles for
flooring, ceiling fans that go click, click and click, and marble
table tops. Almost everyone was eating half-boiled eggs
with dark soya sauce and pepper. Toasted buns with kaya
and butter seemed to be a second favourite. (See, I was
right!) There were also cupcakes, cream cones, swiss rolls
and custard buns. I had the kaya bun. Mum had the half-
boiled egg and kopi.

TAKE-AWAY AT KIM CHOO KUEH CHANG (JUST DOWN THE ROAD) - YUMMY!

Mum said we had to observe 'buying behaviour' at this shop. It was interesting to see cars driving up to park outside the shop, with the drivers dashing in to grab their orders. They bought mostly mini kueh chang and nonya kueh. Boy, these drivers were really fast! But of course – they didn't want to be fined for illegal parking after all! Why didn't anyone ask me to be a look-out for the parking attendant?
I would have done it for free kueh chang.

Mum bought some for me to try. I loved them! Ate six at one go! Mum also bought two boxes home for Ah Kong and Po-Po.

NASI LEMAK AT ADAM ROAD FOOD CENTRE

Mum said we were eating nasi lemak next, a "favourite Malay breakfast food". The food centre was huge. Many stalls with lots of choices for breakfast! Mum checked out the Selera Rasa Nasi Lemak stall. The stall has been rated

Nasi lemak →

Number 1 by many foodies, Mum said. All I know is that there was such a long queue! Everybody was ordering the nasi lemak with a fried chicken wing, otak-otak, fried egg and ikan bilis. The sambal chilli was very good, Mum tried and told me. I ate only the rice and fried chicken wing. Yummy!

NEXT STOP, PRATA AT JALAN KAYU

Mum said we were having prata next. I told her I couldn't eat anymore. But she insisted that I try the prata at Thasevi Famous Jalan Kayu Prata Restaurant. I told her I

Prata with ice cream

believe the stall is famous. No need to try. But she insisted. I ordered it with ice cream. Actually it was quite nice. After eating, I told Mum I had to go home. But she wasn't done yet. She said she wanted to visit a wet market.

While travelling in the car, I thought of wet market smells. Suddenly I felt sick. I told Mum to stop the car. I got out to throw up in the drain. I saw what was left of my undigested kueh chang, nasi lemak and prata ice cream. It was horrible!

Mum felt really sorry after that. We headed home.

Went to bed to rest. Couldn't eat or do anything else the entire day.

Woke up feeling empty in the
stomach. Washed up and got dressed
for school. Sat down for breakfast.
Hmm... I thought maybe kaya toast
with hot Milo would be nice. No such
luck. Breakfast was re-heated kueh
chang, from yesterday.

Ah Kong bought prata and kopi for breakfast this morning.
Thank goodness no more kueh chang! My stomach feels
better just by not having to look at another one of
those things!

I wonder what drink goes well with prata? Hmm... a Milo
drink, hot or iced with lots of Milo powder on it. The Milo
Dinosaur! Let's see, I have seen the Indian uncle at the
drinks stall make it with Milo powder, hot water, condensed
milk and lots of ice. Then sprinkle Milo powder on top.
Maybe I can try adding ice
cream – vanilla or chocolate.
And maybe I can add whipped
cream, the kind squeezed
from a nozzle... sss. I can call
my drink a Milo T-Rex! Or Milo
Godzilla sounds better... Raahh!

What about yogurt instead of ice cream?

Muuuuuuuuuummm... must you read everything
I write? And yogurt with Milo sounds GROSS!

AH KONG'S GUIDE TO COFFEE SHOP KOPI & TEH!

KOPI O/TEH O
Black coffee/tea without milk.

KOPI C/TEH C
Coffee/tea with Carnation evaporated milk. (C stands for Carnation. In Hainanese, "see" also means fresh, as in fresh milk.)

KOPI PENG /TEH PENG
Iced coffee/tea.

This one is really funny!
TAK KEW – MILO!
In Hokkien, tak kew means kicking ball. Ah Kong said that the old Milo commercials on TV used to show someone kicking a ball.

Here's more. These terms are used mostly by Ah Pehs. The same references are used for teh.

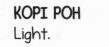

KOPI SIEW TAI
With less sugar.

KOPI POH
Light.

KOPI KOSONG
Black coffee without sugar or milk. In Malay, kosong means empty.

KOPI KAR TAI
With more sugar.

KOPI KOW
Thick. Kow in Hokkien means thick.

TEOH HERGH
Chinese Tea. In Hokkien, this means fishing. The dipping of the tea bag resembles fishing!

AH HUAY
Chrysanthemum tea. In Hokkien, huay means flower.

TAI KA HO
Horlicks. In Cantonese, this means good for everybody!

AMOS' GUIDE TO CAFÉ COFFEE & TEA

AMERICANO

LATTE

TALL

ESPRESSO

CAPPUCCINO

MACCHIATO

CAFFE MOCHA

GRANDE

WHAT'S SO GOOD ABOUT LIVING IN A FLAT?

Mum asked me what makes living in a flat unique?
I suspect it's another assignment. Why is she asking me?
I am only a kid! But since she's my mother, I will help her.

Let's see, I like living in a flat because we get to play along the corridor. We can run and play 'catching'. The flat has a void deck too, which is good for cycling and playing football. Sometimes while waiting for my school bus, I like watching old folks play checkers.

Amos, you should not be playing football! HDB has signs that say No Football!

8pm

What everybody said about living in a flat:

Po-Po said she likes to hang her clothes outside the kitchen window. They dry fast.

Ah Kong said he can have a private garden along the corridor with his potted plants.

Dad said the void deck provides a common space to hold weddings or funerals.

WPI said she likes going to the kindergarten at the ground

floor of our flat. Some of her classmates are also our neighbours.

Mum said she likes the urine detection device in the lift. She calls it a great invention. No one dares to pee in the lift now.

But I'd leave that out. It's got nothing to do with living in a flat. And I think it's a fake. Just a sign to stop people from peeing.

Hmm... Ah Kong said maybe I can try peeing to see if it works.

AMOS! You will do no such thing!

Yes, Mum. I mean NO, I wouldn't dare.

Monday, 14 January

MY BEST FRIENDS AT SCHOOL

After two weeks at school, Dad asked me how I liked my new class. I told him everything was fine. Two of my classmates from the last three years are in the same class as me – Alvin and Anthony.

Ah Kong asked if I chose my friends based on their first names. Maybe I did. I like being called one of the 3As in class. That's us, Amos Lee, Alvin Tan and Anthony Wong. The 3As. We aim to beat the girls in all tests and exams. To be number 1 in class, no less.

Ah Kong said we're number 1 alright – from the bottom of the class. That's true. Last year, I was 28th in class, Alvin was 29th and Anthony was the last boy in class. Anthony's mother cried when he went home with his report card. I was puzzled as it's not like he got retained. He got around 60 marks for each of his subjects – English, Mathematics, Science and Chinese. His mother asked how Alvin and I did, and when he said we were the last three in class, she became upset. She said he should start mixing more with the top kids in class this year. He might get better results.

No. 28
Amos

No. 29
Alvin

No. 30
Anthony
(Last in class)

Wednesday, 6 February

IT'S GOING TO BE CHINESE NEW YEAR!

10pm

Tomorrow is the first day of Chinese New Year! Tonight we had our reunion dinner and Mum said we could stay up to watch the Chinatown countdown on TV.

Po-Po asked what I liked best about Chinese New Year. There are only four things really – pineapple tarts, love letters, kueh lapis and of course, ang pows!

WPI and I got new pyjamas for the New Year. Matching ones. Mum has this thing about getting us matching pyjamas. She thinks it's cute, but no way! I don't mind if WPI wears pyjamas with my favourite cartoon characters, but most of the time, Mum would buy us something that WPI likes. So I end up wearing Dora and Pooh! This is why I will never invite my friends to stay overnight. The whole school would laugh at me if Alvin and Anthony got to see my bedtime wear. The 3As are not called the big mouths for nothing. But only I can laugh at others.

Thursday, 7 February

NEW YEAR VISITING

9pm

I am so tired! We've been out the whole day. I think we must have visited at least 10 families, from Ah Kong and Po-Po's place to the homes of so many aunties and uncles that I don't even know!

But the best part? I collected tons of ang pows!

WPI was really tired and by lunch time, Dad had to carry her around. She couldn't walk any more. She must have been bloated from all the pineapple tarts she ate. But she never throws up when she over-eats.

I saw something interesting today. It was a kid playing A Handheld Gadget. Smart way to keep himself amused. While the adults were talking non-stop and playing mahjong, the boy kept to himself in a corner. I wanted to try The Gadget but he refused to lend it to me. Dad said this was anti-social behaviour. Keeping to himself and playing with The Gadget.

Well, I Just Think The Gadget Is Cool.

Friday, 8 February

THE TRUE SINGAPORE GIRL — AH MENG

6pm

AH MENG HAS DIED!

I was so shocked when Mum told me.

Singapore's most famous orang utan was 48. That's 95 in human years, according to Po-Po.

I feel sad as she was one of my favourite animals in the zoo. We even had breakfast with her once. WPI wasn't born yet and I was basking in all the attention, with Mum, Po-Po and Ah Meng doting on me. Ah Meng had some grapes, watermelons and durians for breakfast. She was a true Singaporean at heart, loving her durians.

Mum said Ah Meng was a true Singapore Girl, a poster girl for Singapore and our world-class zoo. See, just proves that you don't need to be beautiful to be famous. Just need to have orange hair and long limbs.

Mum said that orang utans feel as deeply as we do. I wonder how Ah Meng's children and grandchildren are feeling. They are surely very sad about their mother's death.

WPI came to sit on my bed. She had seen Ah Meng at the zoo once. I told her we are close cousins of the apes. Ah Meng could have been part of our family once upon a time. That got WPI crying.

9pm

It's not just WPI who cried over Ah Meng's death. The whole of Singapore is mourning her death! Amazing. She's only an orang utan.

DRENCHED BY CHAWANG

Mum suggested going to the Night Safari. Let's take a break from New Year visiting, she said. That means fewer ang pows for me, but it's ok because I love the Night Safari. There is always lots to do there. At the entrance, we saw fire-eating natives of the Borneo rainforest. So cool! Mum rushed us quickly into the queue for the tram ride and warned me not to even think of trying to eat fire. Ahem. Would I ever think of that? Ahem.

The tram ride took 45 minutes. It was dark but we could see the animals with special lighting in their enclosures. They were really active.

The rhino, giraffe, tapir, tiger, lion, deer, babirusa (a pig) – we saw them all. But guess who stole the show? It was an Asian elephant named Chawang.

As our tram passed the elephant, he lifted his huge trunk and spat a trunkful of water at us!

We squealed as the water hit us! I could swear that he was gloating from his little trick.

NS Child Admission-T FIT
Admission & Tram to
Night Safari
Date Issued : 09/02/2018 7:20:23 PM
Valid Date : 09/02/2018

Clouded Leopard

Tram Station:

NS   2

At least I got a ticket
for my Guinness World
Records collection.

What a night!

As we left the Night Safari, something
interesting caught my eye - there
was a man sitting in a knee-high
glass tank having his feet nibbled on
by little fishes!

I stood with my jaws wide open.
How interesting! The poster by
the fish spa said that the tiny
toothless fishes are called 'Doctor
Fish' and they feed on dead skin.
It seemed like a fun way to have
your skin taken off... hmm... I
have an idea...

Monday, 11 February

AMOS' FISH SPA

This morning, I woke up before everyone else. I took
Ah Kong's big fish net to catch some of his guppies. I
placed the fishes in a plastic container and hid it in a large
plastic bag.

At recess, I had my plastic bag with me. I grabbed Alvin
and Anthony and brought them to the garden shed. I took
a clean pail and poured Ah Kong's guppies into it. Then I
collected 50 cents from each of them and let them stick
their feet into the pail. I did it too.

Nothing happened. The guppies didn't nibble on our feet.

We waited and dipped our hands and feet into the pail a few times. The guppies darted about, but not a single one came close to our skin. We were so disappointed!

Alvin and Anthony demanded a refund. But I refused. "No refund for services sold!" I said.

They were angry with me, so I decided to give them the guppies to bring home. I made $1 that day. Ah Kong lost six of his guppies, but he didn't know.

Wednesday, 13 February

Alvin and Anthony told me all their guppies died! They called me Doctor Quack. So much for being (en-ter-praising!) (enterprising!)

I am shocked, Amos! You should own up to Ah Kong for stealing his guppies!

Thursday, 14 February

Ah Kong laughed when I told him about stealing his guppies. He said the special fish used in the fish spa are imported from Turkey. They are called Garra Rufa. His guppies cannot do pedicure.

AMOS, DID YOU KNOW THAT SINGAPORE IS THE WORLD'S NUMBER 1 EXPORTER OF ORNAMENTAL FISH?

Now even Dad reads my diary! There is no privacy in this bathroom!

Friday, 15 February

REMEMBERING WORLD WAR TWO

Today my school celebrated Total Defence Day. It's to remember the day Singapore fell to the Japanese during World War Two, in 1942.

It was also our first school outing of the year. I thought we would get to watch an old wartime movie. Alvin, Anthony and I were planning to sit behind the girls and kick at their seats in the cinema! But no such luck. We went to an old car factory in Upper Bukit Timah to visit a World War Two In-ter-pre-ta-tive Centre.

We spent an hour at Memories At Old Ford Factory. Alvin and Anthony were terrified of the graphic descriptions of wartime torture, killing and suffering. I was smart enough to hide in the garden.

There, one of our teachers was talking about what people ate during the war. How exciting. (I mean boring! I am practising the use of (ser-casm) in my writing. I heard Mum calling it dry humour.)

The teacher taught us how to plant yam, sweet potato, sugarcane and rice. How exciting.

I was really hungry when I got home after school. By some strange (coh-in-se-dense,) Po-Po cooked sweet potato porridge with stir-fried yam for lunch! There was also dried shrimp and lots of cabbage. How exciting.

Amos, it's 'sarcasm' and 'coincidence'. You are too young to practise sarcasm in your diary. So please stick to using boring, if that's what you mean.

Mum, my Toilet English Teacher. How exciting.

Saturday, 16 February

Dad said I shouldn't have hid in the garden at the Ford Factory. It's important for me to understand how terrible war is. Maybe when I'm older, I'll appreciate what Ah Kong and Po-Po went through during the war.

Monday, 18 February

NATIONAL DAY PARADE SELECTION

I was chosen as part of a group of 420 school students to perform at the National Day Parade.

I wasn't really keen, but agreed as we were promised that we would not have PE lessons from February to August. We would be practising our NDP performance during PE class.

That's seven months with no physical exercise! Yes! The NDP performance is just a dance anyway, I think. So should be easy. Alvin was excited as he said the NDP gives out the best goody bag ever, with lots of freebies in celebration of National Day! Anthony told his Mum it was compulsory to take part in the NDP. She asked if parents would be given free tickets to watch the NDP. Teacher said no. All parents have to ballot for their tickets online, just like everyone else.

Dad said we are starting National Service early. I wonder what he meant.

Thursday, 21 February

NOT THE NDP BUT THE YOG!

On the news today, saw a huge gathering of people at the Padang, led by the Prime Minister and some other important people. I thought it had something to do with NDP, but boy was I wrong! Dad said Singapore has been chosen to host the world's first Youth Olympic Games, the YOG, in 2010. Sounds exciting enough.

Dad said there would be 3,500 athletes competing from all over the world. There will be the usual sports, like swimming and athletics, but because this is a youth games for 14 to 18-year-olds, there'll be exciting events to watch out for too, like beach wrestling and BMX bike riding.

Hmm... I think they should have chocolate bath wrestling as well. Keeps the energy up and imagine all that yummy gooey stuff to lick off.

Friday, 22 February

ANG POW MONEY

3pm

Yesterday was the last day of Chinese New Year. I opened all my ang pows today and counted $250! Yippee!

9pm

Mum said I must save all my money in the bank. Oh man, it's always like this. Every year, she makes a big show of opening our ang pows and then she will ask Dad to bank in the money for us the next day. Well, it didn't matter last year as there was nothing I wanted to buy. But this year, I thought I could use some of the money to buy something I want. No such luck.

WPI asked why she only had $200. She was crying. Very upset that she had less money than me. Must be those times she was napping at the visitors' homes. Some aunties must have skipped giving her ang pow to save

money. There's no way to
avoid these people. So stingy,
like those people who give only
$2. Actually, someone in my
family does this, but I shall
not name names. Ahem.

*Amos, please don't talk
about Ah Kong like this!
He's already retired and
has no money.*

Sorry Mum! Nothing escapes Mum.

Saturday, 23 February

MY FIRST NDP REHEARSAL

1pm

We were called back to school for our first NDP rehearsal
today. Alvin, Anthony and I were really excited. But it was
quite a let-down. We only managed to get sorted out
according to height, and were assigned to different groups
to report for the next NDP rehearsal.

Two PE teachers were in charge of our rehearsal. While
the prefects were sorting us out by groups, I saw the
teachers practising jumping through hoops and doing
somersaults. I tried to do a somersault too. Alvin tried
standing on his head. All the girls cheered us on. I was
trying to do a second somersault when suddenly one
of the prefects shouted at me. I slipped and fell on my
backside! It was so embarrassing and everyone started
laughing. Thanks to the prefect!

Alvin called to tell me to catch the Chingay Parade floats passing our housing estate. I was really impressed! There were stilt walkers doing somersaults and a lion dance troupe scaling a long pole on a moving float.

Wow, imagine if I could do that at the NDP performance.

9pm

Anthony called. He said he had heard rumours in school that we would be performing a multi-cultural dance for NDP. Oh man, no stilt walking or lion dance act. How lame.

AMOS, DID YOU KNOW THAT CHINGAY WAS INTRODUCED TO ADD FESTIVE CHEER TO THE LUNAR NEW YEAR, WHEN FIRECRACKERS WERE BANNED IN 1972, AFTER A FATAL EXPLOSION THAT KILLED SOME PEOPLE?

This diary is not interested in history!

Sunday, 24 February

DAY OUT WITH DAD

7am

Dad said he has free tickets to watch an air show. I'm really excited as I've never been to one before! We're going to see an A380 plane up close and watch an aerial display of the.... drumroll... Singapore Air Force's Black Knights F-16s! I asked if Alvin could join us as he's really crazy about planes. Dad agreed. So it's WPI, Alvin and I going with Dad. Mum is not into planes.

It took us two hours to get to the Changi Exhibition Centre this morning. We had to take a shuttle bus from Pasir Ris Bus Interchange. Security was tight. Dad said there were 50,000 people trying to get in. All I know is that it was hot and the bag checks took a looooooooooooong time.

I saw one lady faint from the heat while waiting to get through security. And the show hadn't even started yet! Whether it was a ploy or not, she got in fast. The paramedics tended to her and got her in through a special gate.

Later I saw this same lady in the exhibition area, posing for a picture with the actress Zoe Tay! The phony was beaming under her umbrella. Sheesh... I wish I had thought of fainting.

But it was really exciting when the Black Knights flew past! The noise was thunderous! I forgot all about the heat, the fake fainting and the two-hour wait to get in. And when Dad brought us to see the A380, wow, my jaw just dropped. The world's first A380, and Singapore was its new home!

There were other things to see. Alvin and I were really keen to play in the plane simulators, and pretend to be pilots. WPI was just happy collecting free souvenirs. Dad noticed that everybody was happy to give WPI freebies because she looked so cute with her curly hair and straw hat.

Alvin and I decided to drag her along when we wanted to collect freebies. Dad was right – we didn't even have to open our mouths. We just showed WPI, she smiled and everybody would pile her with carrier bags loaded with stuff! We even got free drinks and sweets!

We spotted Zoe Tay again just before we left. She had more fans gathered around her than the President of Singapore. When Zoe's husband, Loo-tenant-Kernal Philip Chee-on, made an appearance, everyone cheered! Wow, imagine that, Zoe Tay and her Black Knight are even more famous than the President.

I'm so glad Dad brought us to the air show. I had lots of fun. So did Alvin. I'm sure WPI enjoyed herself too.

Last I checked, she was counting her freebies on her bed. Dad said she collected 36 key chains, pens and post-it pads. I only had nine!

It's Lieutenant-Colonel Philip Chionh! Do not make fun of people's names, please Amos!

Friday, 29 February

THE PREFECT BULLY

Alvin and I were stopped from going into school this morning. We were late as our school bus got stuck in a traffic jam. We were the last to get down from the bus and as we were running towards the gate, we saw a prefect - the same one who made me fall on my backside at the first NDP rehearsal - slamming the school gate shut! What a bully! I saw him smile as he turned his back to us and then, he just stood there silently guarding the gate, even though he knew we were locked out!

What was worse was having the principal order Alvin and I up on stage. He spoke to all the students about how important it was to be punctual for school.

I was so ANGRY with this prefect! How terrible for Alvin and I. Imagine everyone looking at you, standing beside the principal. I didn't comb my hair this morning. Alvin said he had a hole in one of his socks. He hoped nobody saw that.

Sunday, 2 March

AH KONG & HIS BIRD-FRIENDS

Ah Kong brought me to Ang Mo Kio this morning to meet his friends for a spot of bird-singing. There must have been at least 100 birds strung up high in cages singing their hearts out. Ah Kong rattled off the names of some of the birds – the Sharma, Mata Putih, Straw-Headed Bulbur and Merbok (Zebra Dove). Er... I thought they were pretty. But really, I'm not that into birds.

Mata Putih

One of Ah Kong's friends had also brought his grandson along. The boy was playing with The Gadget! The one I first saw during Chinese New Year! I kept trying to peep over his shoulder to see how to play, but he didn't want to show it to me. I wonder how I can find out more about this thing...

Teacher was so pleased with me today. I told her I went bird-watching with my grandfather at Ang Mo Kio. She said I was a good boy, spending time with Ah Kong and trying to understand his hobby.

That's good, Amos. Ah Kong loves your company!

STILL ON BIRDS

Ah Kong said he wanted to check out a place at Dempsey Hill. He had heard about macaws being kept in an open car park. It sounded interesting enough, so I offered to go with him. Secretly, I was thinking, maybe I'll meet another kid playing with The Gadget!

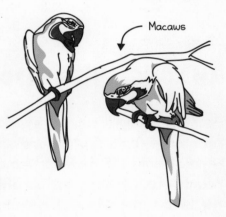

Macaws

Saw 20 macaws feeding on melon seeds and perching on a 'Birds Crossing' sign. I was surprised that they were not chained! Many children were there too, all watching the macaws. I found myself looking around to see if anyone was playing with The Gadget. No such luck though.

Before we left, we stopped at Singapore's largest Ben & Jerry's and Ah Kong bought me an ice cream. Ah Kong asked if I enjoyed feeding the macaws. Actually, it was quite fun and I asked if we could bring one of the birds home.

But Ah Kong said one nagging parrot at home was more than enough. Hmm... would that be Mum?

I am NOT naggy!

Sorry Mum, I think he meant Po-Po then!

Sunday, 9 March

NATURE WATCH

It's the March hols! I love the one-week school break as Mum usually brings us to the bookstores, mostly Borders or Kinokuniya, or to the library to read.

Mum said this time, she'll be bringing us on a nature watch, as part of a new assignment she has to do. Oh man... I hope I won't be puking again!

Monday, 10 March

PRAWNING — NOT FISHING!

9am

Mum said we are going prawning today at some beer garden at Sin Ming Avenue.

Just came back from prawning. It was awful. I had to pick a prawning rod, which is like a fishing rod. Then I had to put the bait on - chicken parts, uncooked. Yucks! WPI refused to do it. So I had to do the dirty job. We threw our lines into the centre of a man-made pond. Then we waited. I thought, so far quite easy. Then I stood there watching old men catch prawns every five minutes! And these were huge prawns! But after half an hour, I caught nothing! Each time I felt something tugging at my bait, I yanked the rod up, to find my chicken part gone!

Mum said I must be patient. Try to focus on the outcome. What outcome? Seeing the prawn hooked onto my bait? Or bragging to Alvin and Anthony that I caught a giant prawn?

I think the bragging outcome worked. I felt a tug at my fishing line almost immediately. I yanked the rod straight up into the air, with a small prawn hooked on my line! Yippee, I did it! Although I had imagined the prawn to be bigger...

WPI wanted to unhook the prawn. I said ok, since I had done the dirty job of putting the bait on for her. But I shouldn't have trusted her. She pulled my prawn off my hook, then THREW it back into the pond!

I screamed so loudly at her that Mum came running over.
I took one hour to catch the prawn and she threw it
back! Mum said it was the right thing to do. We were just
having fun, she said. Oh man...

This is the first and last time I'm going prawning. I can
practise catching Ah Kong's guppies free of charge.

Tuesday, 11 March

FARM VISIT

9am

Mum said we're visiting some farms at Lim Chu Kang today.
I am seriously beginning to dread this assignment of hers.

But WPI was very excited. She said she couldn't wait to
feed goats and do longkang fishing. How is it possible that
we share the same parents? We are so different!

4pm

We set out in the morning. It was drizzling by the time
we got to Hay Dairies. WPI rushed ahead of me. She was
really excited to see the goats. She
couldn't wait to see her friends.

I tagged along behind her, but
stopped when the SMELL hit me.
Yes, the terrible smell. It was
AWFUL! Mum laughed when she
saw me holding my nose. WPI didn't
mind the smell. I'm not surprised.
But she was disappointed that the

goats were in qua-ran-tine. Due for a medical check-up, the people at the farm said.

No feeding of goats was allowed. I was glad to leave. Mum bought some goat's milk for us to try. I liked it. Thick and yummy.

Next stop, we visited a fish farm and did some longkang fishing. For $3, we got to fish for half an hour. Not bad. There were guppies, mollies and other little fishes that we caught with a net. This time, I did better than prawning – I caught six little ones. WPI – zero! Ha ha. I refused to give her any of my fishes. Because we were quarrelling, Mum came over and decided to release all my fishes back! Oh man, not again!

I wanted to go home straight after, but Mum wasn't done. Last stop, she brought us to a frog farm. WPI refused to go near the frogs. She could hear them croaking and she was terrified!

Although I hated the smell, I forced myself to peep at the frogs. It was a gross sight. They were so fat, with bulging eyes, and they were climbing all over one another and leaping about in their enclosure. Mum said they were American Bull Frogs.

American Bull Frog

Just before we left, Mum showed me a half-developed frog. It had only one leg and one eye. I asked WPI if she wanted to kiss the frog. She yelled so loudly that Mum twisted my ear. What did I say wrong? You never know, the mutated frog could be a prince in disguise, even with one leg kicking.

Wednesday, 12 March

RIBBIT! FROGS AND PORRIDGE

I hated the smelly frog farm. But I think frogs are quite interesting animals. Did some research on the internet and found out that we have 23 species of these am-phi-bians in Singapore.

Didn't know that frogs have survived 360 million years. But now they are close to becoming extinct like the dinosaurs.

Frogs react to climate change, pollution and pesticides. Their skin is 'porous' and absorbs con-ta-mi-nants from water easily.

In fact, mutated frogs often indicate extreme changes in the environment. One scientist found frogs with seven toes on their hind limbs! Normal frogs have four toes on each front limb, and five on each hind limb. Also, when frogs are exposed to pesticides, male frogs turn female, while females frogs are unable to produce eggs. Cool facts. I can't wait to tell Alvin and Anthony about frogs!

Ah Kong said he read my diary and would stop eating frogs' legs porridge at Geylang from now.

I thought Ah Kong was convinced of saving the frogs, after seeing how they are being threatened by the environment.

But no. He said he was afraid to eat frogs after reading about the mutated ones with seven toes on one leg. And the half-developed frog we saw, with one leg kicking.

Thursday, 13 March

CRAB HUNTING

Mum said we're going crab-hunting at Sentosa. Now this sounds exciting! Finally, something I like – crab soup. Yummy!

Woke up at 5.30am. WPI couldn't wake up, so Mum left her behind. We drove to Sentosa.

Met a group of nature guides at Siloso Beach. They were called the Naked Hermit Crabs. It was low tide and some children were already wading in the water.

We walked along the shoreline and found lots of pretty corals, sea grasses and small fishes, but only two tiny

crabs! (A Hairy Crab and a Red Egg Crab, the guides said.)
They were so small, I calculated we would need at least
twenty to make a small pot of soup!

As we were looking, one of the little crabs moved, first
to the left, then to the right. Then it heard my stomach
growling and it stopped moving. The crab tucked its claws
under its belly and pretended to play dead! I wanted to pick
it up. But one of the nature guides yelled at me to leave
it alone.

I yelled back that I was catching crabs to make soup.
Everyone stared at me in shock. Mum was red as a
rambutan. She loudly explained to everyone that we were
only observing crabs as part of her assignment. Great.
I was dragged out of bed at 5.30am to appreciate nature.

When no one was looking, Mum picked an empty shell for
me to take home. "A souvenir," she said. But, I placed the
shell back on the beach. If I took it, that would mean one
naked crab, with no home to hide under.

Oh man, no crab for soup. I'm so hungry now!

Thought the hermit crabs were really cute. Found some information on the internet.

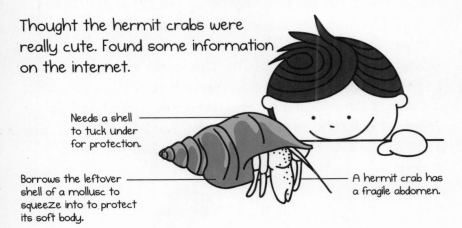

Needs a shell to tuck under for protection.

Borrows the leftover shell of a mollusc to squeeze into to protect its soft body.

A hermit crab has a fragile abdomen.

Checked out the blogsite "www.nakedhermitcrabs.blogspot.com". Lots of interesting stuff there!

Friday, 14 March

LAST DAY OF SCHOOL HOLIDAYS

9am

I'm really glad today is the last day of the holidays. Mum said she would finish typing out her assignment. I have the whole day to myself!

Planning to read all the horror books Alvin lent me. Will watch some TV and call him up later in the afternoon. Maybe can meet him online to play computer games.

4pm

Fell asleep after reading and had a terrible nightmare! Dreamt that I was chased by giant prawns, frogs and hermit crabs. It was gross!

WPI told Mum she heard me screaming in my nap. Mum said it must be all the horror stuff I was reading. My sister, the little rat, squealing on me.

Maybe I shouldn't call her that. She might not want to sleep in the same room as me tonight. Then I'd be really scared. Don't want another nightmare.

Monday, 17 March

HORRIBLE DAY AT SCHOOL

What a day. I was so happy to see my friends back in school. Alvin brought something new to share with us. He was so thrilled with the facts I told him about frogs that he convinced his dad to buy him some to keep as pets. They were so cute! We were watching the frogs in the garden shed when guess who showed up? It was the prefect bully! He said we were not supposed to bring pets to school. We argued that it was only frogs and we needed to learn about them in Science. The terrible boy grabbed Alvin's container of frogs and ran to the toilet. We went after him but we were too slow to stop him from flushing the frogs down the toilet!

We were so shocked by his action! Alvin burst out crying and I felt like hitting the big bully. Anthony was so scared he almost vomited.

The prefect warned us not to bring animals to school again. It was a really cruel act. I thought of complaining to the principal but Alvin said we were not allowed to bring the frogs to school in the first place. So, we will have to keep quiet about this.

I'm going to watch out for this bully. I will get him one day. Prefect or not, he's EVIL.

Friday, 21 March

GREEK STATUES AND THEIR PRIVATE PARTS

Had our second school outing today. Went to see Greek statues at the National Museum.

This exhibition came from the Looov Museum, featuring 130 sculptures and artefacts.

We saw mainly naked Greek statues. Anthony was horrified to see their private parts! There were also some statues without private parts – probably stolen by raiders, Alvin said. Like having your crown jewels robbed. Super funny.

Just as we were leaving, I saw a class of students from our school doodling on their sketch pads. The prefect bully was with the group! When he went to the toilet, Alvin, Anthony and I walked over to take a look at his drawing. It was terrible. He's obviously not an artist. I can do a much better job.

It's the Louvre Museum, Amos! A very famous museum in Paris.

Monday, 24 March

Nude drawings of a Greek statue were pasted in the cubicles of the girls' toilet at school today! No one knew who did it. The drawings looked like the prefect bully, fully naked! How terrible for him.

I enjoyed seeing the Greek exhibition. It was the best school outing we ever had. Learnt so much about the human body, but the best part? Alvin got his revenge.

Amos, did you have anything to do with the nude drawings?

Why would you think that Mum? Ahem.

NO TOILET PAPER IN SCHOOL

Someone removed all the toilet paper from school today!
I only realised it after I had done my big business. I turned
to grab some toilet paper, only to realise that there was
none. I was furious! I had been in such a hurry that I
didn't check to see if there was any toilet paper.

I waited for 15 minutes before Alvin came to the toilet to
look for me. Alvin went looking in every cubicle. There was
no toilet paper at all.

He even sneaked into the girls' toilet. No toilet paper!

I did what I had to do. It was gross. Alvin promised not
to tell anyone what happened in the toilet.

___

7pm

Anthony just called. He
also did his big business
in school today, and
there was no toilet
paper as well! I asked
what he did. He told me
he put his underwear
back on and hoped
no one would smell
anything. I can't believe
how gross he was!

Dear Anthony, you should have done what I did. I took
my underwear out and cleaned my backside with it.

Then I threw it away and just wore my shorts back home. No one smelt anything.

Amos, how many times have I told you to carry tissue paper in your pocket!

9pm

Alvin called. He said maybe the prefect bully was the one who removed all the toilet paper from school today. It's his revenge for being laughed at because of the nude drawings. If that's true, then he's really mean.

Wednesday, 26 March

A SCHOOL PROJECT

We have a recycled art project to do. Alvin, Anthony and I decided we are going to build a robot with recycled materials.

We talked about using three types of materials – mineral water bottles, paper or ice cream sticks.

Amos

Alvin

Anthony

Alvin said in the story of the three little pigs, bricks were the best choice. He wanted to use Lego blocks, but this would not support our theme of recycled art. Besides, I told him we are not pigs. So we decided to use ice cream sticks.

Anthony's mum said we shouldn't eat ice cream just to collect sticks for our project. I had already eaten six ice creams. Alvin had eaten four. Anthony was only on his second ice cream when he vomited. He went home to wash up and his mother scolded him for eating ice cream on an empty stomach.

I decided to choose a different material. Maybe we could use pencils instead.

Alvin suggested that we could go to IKEA to collect free wooden pencils. I told him it was an excellent idea.

Alvin and I made a trip down to IKEA to collect pencils in our bags. Anthony couldn't join us as his mother refused to let him out of the house. I was uneasy that nobody stopped us. It felt like stealing, I told Alvin.

I decided to own up to an IKEA sales person. I returned all the pencils to Customer Service and asked for free wooden pencils. I said it was for a school project. The sales person disappeared to ask his supervisor for advice.

We were both surprised when the guy returned to give us a box of pencils. There were about 200 pencils. That's more than enough to build a robot! We were so happy!

We built our robot in the afternoon. It looks really cool.

Can't wait to hand it in to Teacher on Monday.

Alvin asked if we should include Anthony's name because he didn't help at all. I said yes, as we are all part of the team. We called it the IKEA Robot – "Built to last, not to rust".

Monday, 31 March

Teacher said ours was the best project she had seen. We are so proud of ourselves!

The IKEA Robot was displayed in our school library corner. It had a "Made by the 3As, Singapore" label that Anthony created. Anthony thanked us for including him. He said the label was the least he could do for the project.

You did the right thing, Amos!

I take care of my buddies, Mum.

Tuesday, 1 April

LOCKED OUT OF SCHOOL AGAIN!

We were locked out of school again today! This time, we were on time, but the prefect bully was manning the gate and he shut it when he saw us! It was horrible! He let other students through, but not us! We had to wait till the morning assembly was over, before the gate was opened and the principal came to get us.

He was really angry. He said he would give us one more chance. The next time we are late, he will call our parents down to meet him.

Wednesday, 2 April

Anthony said he heard the prefect bully bragging about how he locked us out of school yesterday.

How mean! This is an abuse of power!

Thursday, 3 April

Mum drove me to school this morning. Maybe I shouldn't have let her. She spoke to the prefect bully and asked if he locked us out of school on Tuesday on purpose. He denied it.

For sure, why would he admit it! I just hope he leaves me alone from now on.

Friday, 4 April

Found out the prefect's name. Michael. He's supposed to be the principal's pet. Must be really smart. The principal likes all the smart children in school.

PEACE IN SCHOOL

Mum asked if Michael was still getting me into trouble. Well, not really. Although some kids in school have started calling me Mummy's boy. I just ignore them.

Michael glares at me when we pass each other in the canteen. But he leaves me alone.

Wonder if he was really affected by the nude drawings. Maybe it wasn't such a good idea. I was just trying to get back at him.

Amos! Please don't provoke the bully again!

Yes, Mum. I'm sorry for what I've done.

BROKEN ROBOT

The 3As were very sad today. Teacher asked us to take our recycled art display home. When we

went to collect it from the library, we saw that our IKEA Robot was broken up! Anthony thought the glue we used wasn't strong enough. But, Alvin and I are convinced that someone broke it up on purpose.

I brought the robot home. Ah Kong helped me to fix it.

At least it looks as good as new now! Hope Alvin will be really pleased to see it on Monday!

Alvin said he didn't want the robot anymore. Anthony said he would be happy to keep it in his house. He promised to take good care of it.

Anthony said he didn't want the robot. He kept having nightmares at night, thinking that the robot would come alive. I took the robot back. I gave it to WPI.

WPI slept like a pig through the night. I could hardly sleep. I kept having these weird dreams about the robot coming alive. Plus I kept thinking about Michael, the prefect bully. How horrible of him, if it is really true that he broke our robot!

Mum asked why I placed the robot in the recycling bag. I told her I didn't want it anymore. She said she would break the robot apart, and I would have more pencils to write this diary with. Oh man...

Yes Amos, don't waste all those pencils!

MUM'S DAY OUT AND MY SUFFERING

Mum said she would give me something to write about, since I've been saying nothing much has been happening at school. I suspect it's another assignment. We are going to Sentosa today. I hope we are not going to the beach. I don't really like the sun.

Mum said she had to review riding the Luge, taking the cable car, or visiting the Images of Singapore. See, I was right! Another one of her assignments.

I said no to the cable car, as I don't really like looking down from heights. As for the Images of Singapore, I wasn't

in the mood to learn about history. I asked why we couldn't visit the Underwater World. Mum said we've been there so many times, the sharks can recognise me by now. Mum can be so corny sometimes.

HI AMOS

So we rode the Luge today. Now what Mum failed to tell me was that at the end of riding the Luge was this skyride, which took us back OVER the hilltop to where we first started.

AND THIS WAS WORSE THAN TAKING THE CABLE CAR!

There was no cover. We had to sit on a revolving bench, with our feet dangling high above the tree tops! And at the highest point of the ride, the thing stopped. Yes, to give us a bird's eye view of the area! WPI was so excited she couldn't stop talking and pointing. I was too nervous to look down!

And when I took a peek, I saw a monitor lizard lurking among the trees. I wasn't quite sure. But it was moving so slowly that I knew it couldn't be a human crawling. I had to stop looking down as I felt like vomiting.

It took about five minutes to get back to the station, the worst time of my life!

Monitor lizard baits

Monitor lizard

Mum and WPI were "ooh"-ing and "aah"-ing over the view of Siloso Beach and the Rasa Sentosa Resort. WPI was also excited when she spotted an eagle in the sky.

I was just afraid of crashing and becoming lizard bait.

WPI loved the skyride so much that she wanted to have a second go. I refused! I had more than enough excitement for the day.

Po-Po helped Mum to wash our clothes tonight. She asked why my shorts smelt of urine. I told her it must be the new soap powder Mum bought.

Ah Kong asked if we tried the Flying Trapeze at Sentosa. I told him not to mention that to Mum. That's the last thing I want to try. I will stick to watching the sharks at the Underwater World.

At least I got another ticket for my Guinness World Records collection!

Monday, 12 May

EARTHQUAKE IN CHINA

Something terrible happened in China. A major earthquake hit the coastal city of Sichuan, flattening buildings, burying people and killing thousands!

We saw the disaster on TV. I felt so sorry for those people trapped in the quake.

Po-Po was in tears when she saw rescue efforts being hampered by rain and massive landslides.

Mum and Ah Kong had the TV switched on the whole night, to watch the news for more updates.

At dinner, everyone ate in silence. Including WPI. She must have known something terrible had happened. She didn't ask her usual irritating questions.

Tuesday, 13 May

Last night in bed, I had a terrible feeling about the quake. As I saw parents wailing for their kids trapped under collapsed schools, I suddenly understood how much Dad and Mum love us. No one wishes for this to happen. It was an act of nature, Dad said.

I went over to WPI's bed and hugged her. She went on sleeping soundly. I went over to Dad and Mum's room. They were still awake. I asked if I could do something for the quake victims. Mum suggested that I could donate some money to help with the rescue efforts. I thought that was a good idea.

Wednesday, 14 May

This morning in school, most of us had brought money from home to hand in to our teachers. I had called Alvin and Anthony last night and told them to bring some money as well. Our donation was made to the China Earthquake Fund, managed by the Singapore Red Cross.

As I stood in the assembly hall, listening to the principal giving his morning address, I realised how lucky I am to be living in Singapore.

I go to school, I have friends like Alvin and Anthony, I have loving parents and Ah Kong and Po-Po who dote on me. Although I don't always get to buy the things I want, and I hate studying for exams, I wouldn't want to be anywhere else in the world right now.

Thursday, 15 May

OUR NDP REHEARSALS

It's back to our NDP rehearsals after our mid-year exams. I've lost count of the number of times we've practised since February.

We still can't quite figure out what we will be doing. Just lots of flapping arm movements, jumping jacks and pecking poses. It's supposed to be a multi-cultural dance. But I don't see how the Malay, Indian or Chinese parts come in. The music is some funky aerobics beat. Nothing multi-cultural either.

Saw a student playing with The Gadget while waiting for the rehearsal to start. This time, I was in luck - the boy was nice enough to show me what he was doing with it. Hmmm... it's so cool!

Thank goodness we didn't see Michael today. He would be so eager to report us to the principal. We're not supposed to bring expensive gadgets to school, not even handphones!

Friday, 23 May

LAST DAY OF SCHOOL!

Finally, we can stop our NDP rehearsals! Today is the last time we will be practising our NDP performance. Rehearsals resume after the holidays.

I spoke to the boy with The Gadget today. He let me play with it. I like it very much! It's very fun. I have decided - I'm going to earn some money during the holidays to buy this thing.

AMOS LEE'S TOP THREE FOODS

Mum asked me to help her with her new assignment today – name three eating experiences a kid my age would love.

Let's see, my favourite foods right now are Old Chang Kee curry puffs, IKEA meat balls and fried chicken wings (I need to have them together!), prata with sugar or curry, pineapple tart ice cream, and mini kueh chang. There's also McDonald's hot cakes, fried carrot cake and satay.

But Mum said the food I choose must come with an "experience". Yikes.

Let's see, with McDonald's, I've always enjoyed getting a Happy Meal with a toy, and the free balloons. With fried carrot cake, prata and satay, it's the "experience" of eating at a hawker centre. Nothing new really. With Old Chang Kee, it's mostly grab and go. A quick bite before tuition.

I've decided that my ranking will be:

1. **EATING MEATBALLS AND FRIED CHICKEN WINGS AT IKEA.** Plus an hour of fun in Smaland each time we visit – the FREE indoor play area with WPI's favourite ball play!

2. HAVING PINEAPPLE TART ICE CREAM AT ISLAND CREAMERY.

WPI and I love to visit Serene Centre for local ice cream flavours. Mum likes the teh tarik and pulut hitam flavoured ice cream. WPI and I just love the pineapple tart flavour.

3. EATING MINI KUEH CHANG FROM KIM CHOO, A QUAINT PERANAKAN PLACE

(But cannot eat six at one go.)

I can't wait to see my suggestions published. Maybe these three places will offer me free treats each time I visit. Cool!

Mini kueh chang

Friday, 30 May

Mum submitted the article to her editor today and told me something amazing. In a survey IKEA did with 8,000 respondents, its meatballs were listed among the top three favourite foods. See, I'm always right about food. In Amos' favourite foods list, IKEA's meatballs are rated Number 1!

Monday, 9 June

REMEMBERING A T-REX NAMED SUE

The 3As celebrated our 3rd anniversary of knowing each other today. We got together at Anthony's place. His mum made us Milo Dinosaurs and huge chocolate chip cookies. Yummy!

This time three years ago, we went on a school excursion and visited an exhibition at the Singapore Science Centre.

It was the "Dinosaurs – a T-Rex named Sue and Friends" exhibition. There under the jaws of Sue, we made a pact to stick together against all girls!

Cretaceous!

Sue was a T-Rex that lived in the ~~Crusty-sheeshee~~ period. When she was alive, she weighed seven tonnes! Her fossils are the largest and most complete of a T-Rex ever found.

This is how tiny the three of us looked, under the jaws of Sue:

I found it amazing that a female T-Rex could look so menacing! Imagine if she could talk, she would be a monster of a mother! No need to nag, just roaaarrrr and her children would listen to everything she says.

My favourite pose:

This is how I look, writing in my diary. Mum is the T-Rex, waiting to bite my head off, in case I take too long. "No piles, Amos!"

Tuesday, 10 June

MAD ABOUT FOOD

Yesterday, I told Alvin and Anthony about how much I wanted to earn money to buy The Gadget. They were really excited when I told them I'd share my new purchase with them. We decided to raise money by producing a food guide ourselves and selling it.

Dad told us about a poll for the top 20 Favourite Hawkers which the Straits Times STOMP portal is holding. Anthony said there were food blogs we could check out too. Mum said we could visit the library to look for guide books or restaurant guides. Dad said we could use his colour printer to print copies of the Food Guide.

We decided to sell our Food Guide for 50 cents each. Wow, that's easy money to make! Cheap and good.

Wednesday, 11 June

Anthony passed all his research to Alvin, who's in charge of writing the guide. I'm designing the flyer. We produced

10 copies of the Food Guide.
Dad brought them to his office
and sold everything to his
colleagues! We made $5! Yeah!

Dad told me about this food blog.
I love it because the pictures
make me drool!

www.ieatishootipost.sg

Thursday, 12 June

ME, AN ENTREPRENEUR!

We're launching Project PSP officially today. We have
$5 for a start. Mum asked me what's Project PSP. It's a
secret! Something that I've been eyeing for a long time.
It's something that will be shared with the 3As.

Alvin suggested we combine our art skills by painting on
T-shirts to sell. The two of us are the best in art in our
class. Mum said we could use her old acrylic paint. It's
Mum's passion – painting. Maybe I inherited my talent from
her. Went to the market to buy five plain white tees. They
only cost $5 each, all kids' sizes. Spent the whole afternoon
painting with Alvin. Anthony came over to help too.

Here're some
of our
T-shirt designs:

We decided on "Food, Our First Love". See, we have designs inspired by the swirl of the mee goreng and the brown spots from a perfect prata. Mum said it could be spaghetti or even tiramisu. That's it, art is open to interpretation. It's what we feel when we connect with it. We're selling our T-shirts at $15 each. That's three times what I paid for each one.

Mum said we can also try painting on white canvas shoes to sell.

Friday, 13 June

We went to school to sell our mee goreng and prata T-shirts. There were students attending holiday classes in school. But we didn't get to sell anything because Michael was in school today. He stopped us by saying that he'd report us to the principal.

We left for home, with all our T-shirts.

Sunday, 15 June

WPI helped me to paint five new T-shirts which Mum bought. Mum called her style graffiti art. It's just messy art, with no theme. I can't even see what she drew or painted! She also took care of painting all the 10 pairs of canvas shoes Mum bought.

I can't believe it. We managed to avoid Michael today and I sold all of WPI's designs! That's five T-shirts and 10 pairs of canvas shoes. I'm rich, I'm rich, I'm rich!

Alvin called WPI a true genius. I shall not be jealous.

Closer to reaching my goal for Project PSP now, thanks to WPI. I can't believe it. Looks like we do have something in common after all!

My sums:
$15 x 5 tees
$12 x 10 pairs of shoes
$5 from selling the Food Guide

Total $200

The principal called Mum today. He said he had heard about me selling stuff in school. Mum told him I was only trying to be enterprising. He said if our family needed money, he could recommend that I receive an allowance from the Straits Times School Pocket Money Fund, which hands out pocket money to needy students. Mum told me to stop selling things at school. She's upset that the principal thought I needed money badly.

Must be Michael who told the principal. Trying to get me into trouble, again!

Thought of another way to make money.

I offered to wash Dad's car. He said he wouldn't pay me for my service. I offered to wash my neighbour's car. Uncle asked if I needed money badly. Mum overheard our conversation and she was very angry with me.

She warned me that if she caught me begging for money again (but I didn't!), she'd keep all of my $200.

I have to look for another way.

VALUE-FOR-MONEY HOLIDAY COURSES

Mum signed WPI and I up for two courses at the Community Centre. I suspect it's another assignment.

I went for a Science workshop where I learnt to build a water rocket, with a plastic bottle. Using the power of soda combined with mint, we created a burst of energy to propel a bottle (our water rocket) across a basin of water. Cool!

WPI went for a Little Chef class, where she learnt to make her own sushi. Ah Kong and I were smart enough not to eat her sushi. Mum said we hurt her

feelings. Well, better safe than sorry. How much does a five year old know about ~~hi-gin?~~ *hygiene!*

I was right about the assignment. Mum said the CC responded to her query for value-for-money holiday courses by recommending the water rocket and sushi classes. They were educational, fun and cheap! Mum spent less than $20 on each of us.

Dad said Mum knows all the programmes of the CC very well. WPI goes for ballet classes every Sunday. That's where Mum spends her Sunday mornings talking to other mums, finding out what's new, what's cheap, and what's fun to do at the CC. If any of these mums have something to complain about the courses, Mum will be assigned to write in. There'd be a long letter from her to answer to, the poor things at the CC.

YEP, THAT'S HOW THE PUBLIC KEEPS PUBLIC AGENCIES IN CHECK. THROUGH COMPLAINTS.

Your father is always sensitive about receiving complaints. He thinks he's the best in his job. No one can fault him.

Why is everyone reading and leaving comments in my diary! It's supposed to be private!

SHOW & TELL

8am

Tomorrow we go back to school. We have a Show
& Tell session at assembly. I thought of appearing as
a durian. Why not? And I have the perfect song to go
along with it. Sing it to: "The more we are together,
together, together..."

"Have you ever smelled a durian, a
durian, a durian...?"

"So thorny, but deli-cious, so smelly,
but yummy..."

I just know I'm going to be a star
at school tomorrow ha! Now I only
need a durian suit.

3pm

Mum didn't agree with my choice for Show & Tell.
She said it's a silly idea and she doesn't know how to
make a durian suit. But she said she came across an
article in the newspapers about the plight of the pan-go-lin.
She offered to scan the article and print out a picture of
the pangolin for me. She said I can talk about the
pangolin instead.

Hmmm... it's "thorny", with scales not spikes. It's a
mammal found in Asia and Africa, and what I like best
is that it has a 25cm long tongue to lick up ants and
termites for food! Wow, cool!

Mum and I did up a big
poster on the pangolin.

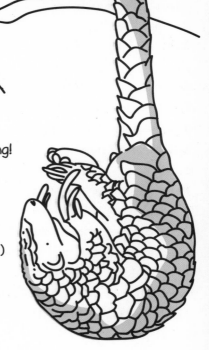

THE SCALY PANGOLIN — CLAIM TO FAME?

* Has the longest tongue among all mammals – 25cm long!
* About 75cm to 1m long, only about 50 pangolins left in Singapore's forests!
* Eats ants and termites.
* Rolls up into a ball (like a durian?) when threatened.
* Has large claws on paws – "feet".

MYTH OF PANGOLIN?

Scales are made of ke-ra-tin, same as our fingernails.
No medicinal remedy for rheumatism, liver, stomach or
skin problems! (This line is from Mum.)

So don't catch and kill them. Eat a durian instead ha!
(This line is from me.)

Monday, 23 June

I was the BIGGEST STAR in school today! Teacher was so
proud of me. She said my talk was better than the one
done by the "Zoo Goes to School" programme!

I was really happy, till I bumped into Michael after school.
I had kind of forgotten all about him during the holidays.

He called me a freak.
He said I looked like
the pangolin, all round
and weird. Alvin and
Anthony were with me.
The three of us ignored
him and just walked off.
I felt really hurt.

Mum said the best way
to deal with a bully is
not to let it show that
whatever was said
affected me. She asked if I needed her to speak to Michael
again. I told her I would deal with my own problems.
Nothing that I can't handle.

You did right, Amos!
Just walk away from the bully.

Sunday, 29 June

LEAVE NO BOOK UNTURNED!

Mum said she was going to bring us to a big event, something
with as large a turn out as the National Day Parade.

We only found out when we got to the Singapore Expo.
It was the National Library Book Sale.

It should be called The Great Singapore Sale. Mum told
us there were 400,000 used books on sale. Prices started
from $1.

Mum disappeared to look at books. She left me with WPI. I told WPI to stand in a corner, as I wanted to look for books on how to make money.

Half an hour later, I returned to the spot where I left her. Imagine my shock when I didn't see her! I had terrible images of myself being punished by Mum! I ran around yelling for WPI. I kept looking out for her curly head. Finally, I saw a crowd of aunties gathered at the children's section, comforting a little girl. I walked closer and saw WPI crying. She was all red in the face, with mucus pouring from her nose. I felt so sorry! I ran up to her and hugged her tight. The poor thing...

Mum came looking for us later. By then WPI had stopped crying. Mum had four boxes of books. I could see her handwriting on the boxes. Amos – English, Science & Mathematics for school, Amos – Chinese for school. Mei Mei – Storybooks, Dad – Comics.

So unfair! Mine were all related to school work and studies. WPI and Dad got all the fun stuff!

Mum asked WPI why her eyes were red. She kept quiet and didn't say anything.

I could have kissed her! She didn't tell Mum I left her alone!

We paid for our books and left the place. Mum took two comics out of Dad's box and passed them to me. Out of 400,000 books in the National Library Book Sale, I only got two that I don't mind reading. We could have gone to Popular bookshop, and saved the time queuing.

Amos, you should be glad I didn't punish you for leaving your sister alone!

Maybe writing everything in this diary isn't a good idea. But I realised something today. Mei Mei is still my sister. I'd have hated myself if I lost her for good.

Sunday, 13 July

MUM'S CAR BOOT SALE

8am

I thought the National Library Book Sale was the last we saw of sales. Boy, was I wrong.

Mum signed up to take part in a car boot sale. She had this crazy idea of selling all her old dresses. Everyone in the family complained about having to support her at this sale. But I thought it was quite a good idea – I could raise money for Project PSP by selling some books! Alvin said he would join me. We plan to be clowns for the day and charge children money for doing balloon twisting. Ah Kong said he would sell his old records. Po-Po brought out her secret stash of beauty products. I gathered all the cheap books Mum got from the library sale. Perfect!

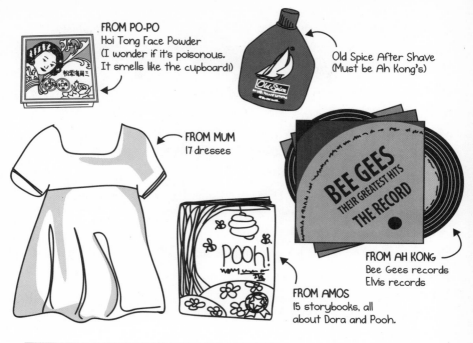

FROM PO-PO
Hoi Tong Face Powder
(I wonder if it's poisonous.
It smells like the cupboard!)

Old Spice After Shave
(Must be Ah Kong's)

FROM MUM
17 dresses

BEE GEES
THEIR GREATEST HITS
THE RECORD

FROM AH KONG
Bee Gees records
Elvis records

POOh!

FROM AMOS
15 storybooks, all
about Dora and Pooh.

7pm

Just got back from the car boot sale. It was quite
interesting, like a pasar malam. Goods were sold from the
back of our car boot.

There were about 60 cars,
selling books mostly. Some
people were also selling stuffed
toys, bags, shoes, even radios!

Many children came to see
what Alvin and I were doing
with the balloons. I was really
lousy. I kept bursting my
balloons. Alvin could only do space rings. He said he got the
idea from an alien. Some children actually believed him
and paid him $2 for a space hat. I told him it was bad
to tell a lie. But he was such a clown! Really funny. WPI

looked really cute wearing some of his creations. I think that helped to draw children to our car.

It was such a long day. There were so many people at the car boot sale. But we didn't sell anything! Not my books, or Mum's clothes, or any of Ah Kong's and Po-Po's stuff. But Alvin, yes, ALVIN made $80! That means he sold 40 space hats! Oh man...

Dad said it was the first time we did this as a family. It's the bonding that's important, not how much money we make. I guess it's true. It was fun running a stall for the day.

Amos, please return all of your sister's books to her!

Nothing escapes my mother.

Friday, 18 July

CLOWNING FOR A BIRTHDAY PARTY

I can't believe my luck! A lady called Mum and asked if Alvin and I would like to dress up for her son's birthday party! She had seen us selling balloons last week at the car boot sale.

Would we? But of course! This is a golden chance to raise funds for Project PSP!

She said she would pay me $10 an hour, plus $80 extra to rent a costume. I promised her that Alvin would learn how to twist balloon dogs and swords by the day of her son's birthday.

We took a trip to Haji Lane. Walked through Arab Street, then got to Aliwal Street, where Mum brought me to the No. 1 Costume shop to rent an outfit for my new job.

It was like walking onto a huge movie studio set. We saw all kinds of costumes – Disney, Looney Tunes, gingerbread men, even weird uniforms like police and crooks, doctors and nurses, fairies and demons, and different animal suits! I asked to see a clown suit. I was shocked to see it being so, so... clownish! It was an awful red, purple and pink, with a giant checkered bow tie. No way I was going to wear this suit, even if it's to earn $10 an hour!

I looked around and found some suits that I liked – a monkey suit, a dragonfly suit and a vampire bat suit. Mum said it's not Halloween, so I dropped the vampire bat suit. The monkey suit was missing a tail, so I took the tail from the dragonfly suit and stuck it on the monkey suit.

I practised my act with Alvin and Anthony's help. They downloaded a tune of the Green Hornet on Anthony's MP3 player and we blasted it on the computer speaker. I learnt to twitch my body, scratch my armpits and jog around in circles, dancing to the Green Hornet. I'm going to be really good at the party!

Alvin has been bursting one balloon every five minutes. He's really not good at this balloon twisting thing.

Saturday, 26 July

The lady screamed when she saw me in my monkey suit. Then she started laughing. Her four-year-old loved my costume! All the kids wanted to pull my dragonfly tail.

I made everyone queue up to pull my tail, take a picture and then get their faces painted. It was easy. I only had to draw whiskers. They were all either cats or mice. Alvin could only twist balloon rings as hats.

I was at the party for five hours and everyone loved my monkey dance! I left with $50 in my pocket. But what's more important is that I have bookings for two more parties. One mum wanted me to be a pirate. Another mum wanted me to be Merlin the wizard. Alvin wasn't wanted.

Monday, 28 July

11am

Mum drove me to the No. 1 Costume shop again. I had a hard time picking out a wizard suit. The pirate one was easy. I even had a pirate's hat. In the end, I rented a vampire bat suit.

2pm

I drew silver stars and pasted them on my vampire cape. From Dracula to Merlin!

Saturday, 2 August

A PIRATE PARTY

The pirate party was held at a condominium pool. It was quite fun! There were ship-printed plates and cups. Water games were held in the pool and all I had to do was blow the whistle when a kid got out of line. A pirate referee! When each kid left the party, they got a chest of golden chocolate coins.

But the best part was that everyone had to wear a pirate's eye patch. Some kids had eye patches cut out of eye masks taken from planes, other kids had black eyes painted on. The party was a blast!

WIZARD WITH NO MAGIC

I was a wizard for the day. The kids expected me to do some magic tricks. All I could manage was to wave my hands and ask for food or prizes to be presented. Quite lame actually. I felt lousy as I didn't prepare for this party.

When I spied a piano in a corner of the house, I asked one of the mums to play the Green Hornet tune.

The kids watched as I went crazy, twitching my body, scratching my armpits and running around stinging the air with my backside.

Most of the kids were laughing and enjoying themselves, except for one smart aleck.

This boy stood up and screamed at me. "You copy cat! You stole the dance from the monkey boy!"

I didn't know I had a fan. So much for trying to explain that I was the monkey boy.

My career as a birthday clown ended that afternoon. But I was $150 richer, from three parties.

FOR PROJECT PSP
$200 + $150 = $350 (Took $20 out to buy Alvin a book, The Idiot's Guide to Balloon Art.) Left with $330.

9pm

Anthony called. He said he checked with his dad and $330 is enough to buy The Gadget, but not enough to buy the software and games to play on The Gadget! Looks like I will have to keep raising money!

Monday, 4 August

BIRD FOR THE DAY!

After seven months of training for the National Day Parade, we finally got to see our costumes. They are BRIGHT YELLOW! And each of us will have a BEAK strapped to our face. We are supposed to be giant flapping birds! And, we will be wearing bandanas made of sari, batik and silk. That's the multi-cultural bit in this performance.

Now I understand why we've been asked to do so many flapping arm movements, jumping jacks and pecking poses. But how is this supposed to make us proud of being Singaporean?

We spent four hours in the hot sun today, jumping, flapping our arms and screeching, "We love you Singapore!" We were so sweaty and itchy, and the yellow paint on our faces made us a laughing stork! (stock!)

The children in the item before ours were dressed as warriors! They even got to have war paint slapped on their faces – green and brown. Not yellow like ridiculous birds.

This is the first and last time I volunteer to take part in the National Day Parade.

Tuesday, 5 August

Anthony said he got his mother to write a letter to Teacher. He will not be taking part in NDP. He said he was going to be sick on Saturday. Sheesh...

Friday, 8 August

Rumours were going round that the Warriors would not be allowed to carry their swords. Something about a security threat.

Saturday, 9 August

It's true! The Warriors were given umbrellas!

Hooray! We were not the only ones looking stupid on National Day.

But the BEST part was seeing Michael today. The principal's pet got to dress up as the Chief Bird of the contingent. HA HA HA... It was so funny! Alvin and I had a good time laughing. That really made our day.

Sunday, 10 August

Woke up at 11am. Mum allowed me to sleep in late. She said I did her proud. Actually last night was quite magical. As we sang for the grand finale, with the fireworks exploding above us, my chest felt heavy. I looked around and saw some of my school mates crying. Could be glad that our torture was over. The school promised that we could collect our goody bags on Monday. Looking forward to that.

Monday, 11 August

I'm so HAPPY! We got to collect our NDP goody bags. I divided the freebies into - "For Po-Po and Mum" (NEWater, discount coupons for restaurant meals and spa treatments and a bottle of AXE brand medicated oil), "For WPI" (wet tissue, poncho and trash bag), and "For Amos" (two giant inflatable gloves, tattoos, stickers, cap, biscuits, sweets and of course, the Singapore flag).

This was worth the seven months of training! Anthony was so jealous of our freebies. Well, too bad. No sweat, no gain.

Po-Po scolded me for giving her NEWater. She said she doesn't want to drink recycled water. "Ayer jamban" she called it. I think that is Malay for water from the toilet bowl.

Dad said NEWater is used-water collected in treatment plants, filtered with mem-brane technology, whatever that is. I think it just means the water is safe to drink.

Po-Po is being silly! I made a big show of popping open the bottle and drinking up the NEWater in front of her.

Tuesday, 12 August

I can't believe it. Po-Po woke me up at 6am this morning to ask if I feel like I'm having die-o-rear!

It's diarrhoea, Amos! And yes, Po-Po is being silly. NEWater is perfectly safe!

Sunday, 17 August

OLYMPIC STARS

FASTEST MAN ON EARTH

It's been an exciting week. Everyone has been glued to the TV watching the Beijing Olympic Games, me included!

Today, I witnessed a human bolt of lightning! The fastest man on earth, Usain Bolt from Jamaica, in his yellow and green tank top. Dad warned us to keep our eyes on the TV. "It'll be over before you realise it!" He was right! Usain took 9.69 seconds to finish his run – that's faster than I can pee! Two seconds down, seven seconds to pee, another two seconds to pull my trousers back up! 11 seconds in total! WPI also tried peeing. We timed her. She took 20 seconds. What a slow poke! Mum said it was a disgusting experiment.

The 100m dash is Dad's favourite sport because he was a sprinter when he was young. He told everybody proudly that he remembers running at the National Stadium, with thousands of people cheering him on. Wow, imagine that. My dad, a sports hero!

AMOS, DID YOU KNOW THAT THE SUIT THAT USAIN WORE WAS MADE IN SINGAPORE?

Wow I'm impressed! The world's fastest runner, with help from Singapore. Cool!

FASTEST MAN IN WATER

I've been watching the swimming events closely as unlike Dad, my favourite sport is swimming. I like the water as I feel weightless and I can move without much effort. (I hate jogging as I can feel my fats rolling about as I run.) I can't believe that

Michael Phelps won eight gold medals! Oh man... he was like a water machine. Dad said it was focus and hard work that made him win. I don't think I will ever have what it takes to be a sports hero. But I love swimming and that's good enough for me.

Monday, 18 August

PING PONG

I've always thought that table tennis was pretty boring – the ball is so small, I get a headache keeping track of where it is! But yesterday's match was different. We were all rooting for Singapore in the Table Tennis Finals! Even WPI, who usually hates sports, was jumping up and down on the sofa, cheering!

Ah Kong said we have been waiting 48 years to win an Olympic medal. So long? No wonder when Team Singapore came in second, all our neighbours cheered and clapped so loudly. Ha ha... actually, my family was doing the same thing too!

Team Singapore was led by Li Jiawei, Wang Yuegu and Feng Tianwei. As the Majulah Singapura played when our players received their silver medal, I felt so proud of Singapore. I told Dad that maybe I will pick up table tennis too!

Tuesday, 19 August

OLYMPIC STARS IN SINGAPORE?

I wonder if any Olympic Stars will visit Singapore during the Youth Olympic Games in 2010? I must find a way to work as a bell boy in the Youth Olympic Village so that I can find out who's staying where and get everybody's autograph. Then I can design T-shirts with famous autographs on them and sell them for lots and lots of money!

Maybe I should write a letter to the Minister in charge of the YOG and suggest that we should have a few Olympic Stars visit Singapore to support children in money-making ventures.

Amos, they should inspire our athletes in sports excellence and nothing else!

Mum, it's just a wild idea! Maybe not a letter. I will send a copy of this entire diary to the Minister. He will ask why my mother makes me write in the bathroom!

Amos, you will do no such thing!

SLIPPER NATION

I saw an incredible picture in the newspapers of Usain Bolt with a pair of golden shoes! Boy, so cool to be the fastest man on earth with shoes like that!

Amos Lee, however, prefers wearing slippers. Yup, in bright and sunny Singapore, it's cooler to wear slippers. Everybody does. Alvin, Anthony, even WPI. Slippers are so easy to slip on. No need to dirty our hands with wearing socks and shoes.

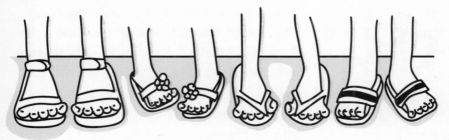

But going to school, that's a different story. It's compulsory to wear white shoes. I used to have school shoes with velcro, until Mum asked me to tie a knot one day and I told her I didn't know how to. She freaked out and said from that day onwards, I would have to wear school shoes, with laces! Imagine, the school bus would be waiting downstairs with the driver honking loudly, and I would be struggling with tying my laces.

Mum would stand over me watching and refusing to help me. She would be yelling at me to hurry up, while signalling from the fourth floor to the bus driver to wait. Then after I wore my shoes, I would have to run down four floors!

These days, I am smarter. I tie a tight, dead knot for the butterfly lace, and leave enough space to slip my foot in and out of the shoe.

Anyway, about slippers... if we go to the hawker centre, NTUC, library, swimming or tuition, Mum will allow us to wear slippers. But if it's anywhere further than Toa Payoh, like to Orchard Road for shopping, she said we must wear shoes, with socks. WPI and I will whine and complain. But she always says no, we must dress well. "Never know who you might meet!"

I wonder who she thinks we might meet. The Prime Minister? One day when I become the Prime Minister, I will pass a law that says all children can wear slippers to school. And all teachers and parents MUST wear socks with shoes and laces.

Monday, 15 September

THE WORLD'S FIRST NIGHT RACE

It's a week before the world's first Grand Prix night race is taking place in Singapore. Although I don't understand what the fuss is about, I can feel the excitement already. Ah Kong has been bugging Po-Po to give him an advance on his allowance to buy a ticket to watch the Grand Prix. But Po-Po refused. Mum? She is just as excited buying

PIT STOP
CAKE

FERRABERRI

F1-related merchandise. I've
seen her bring home two
Ferrari key rings, a 'pit stop
cake' for breakfast and a
Ferraberri – a crass-ont with
strawberries and chocolate
chiffon wheels!

Croissant, Amos, croissant!

Mum's F1 shopping madness continues! She just came
home and gave me an F1 polo shirt. Now this is shopping
madness I don't mind! All I need is a matching cap and
an F1 car! Watch out everybody! Amos Lee, the driver of
super fast F1 cars! Vrooom!

I couldn't believe it! Mum
dragged us all to Ang Mo Kio
Hub to buy another 'pit stop
cake', and guess what? There
was a racing car simulator
there, in front of NTUC of all
places! While Mum was buying

more stuff, Dad and I hopped into the simulator for a
few rounds of pretend-driving. I was so excited when Dad
whipped out his camera and asked me to pose with the
'F1 car'. Yipppeee! And I was wearing my F1 polo shirt too!
I think I seriously looked like a very cool F1 driver!

THE SINGAPORE GRAND PRIX

We watched the race on TV. I didn't understand what was going on, but just cheered whenever I saw a Ferrari leading. Ha ha...

Mum was only interested in picking out the Singapore icons against the night sky. She kept pointing them out – Singapore Flyer, Esplanade, Fullerton Hotel, Padang... Yes, Mum. Yes, Mum.

In the meantime, Ah Kong and Dad were glued to the TV set. Both of them shouted when an accident happened at the pit stop – a Ferrari drove off, trailing a fuel hose. Wow, I yelled, a Dr Octopus-Ferrari!

But no one laughed. Dad looked like he was going to cry.

When I went to bed, I saw some books on my study table. I should have guessed. It wasn't enough for Mum to buy F1 stuff. She had to go down to the library to borrow books on F1 too. She wrote me a note, "Read these books and write about your biggest impression of F1."

Well, my biggest memory is getting my picture taken with the racing car simulator. That was super cool! As for the race itself, sure cranked up the electricity bill for the whole of Singapore! Oh, and also added to global warming as well! Ha ha...

F1 FEVER RAGES ON

3pm

Mum brought us for high tea at the Royal Plaza On Scotts – she was there to meet someone for an interview for an assignment. We were quite excited to see a life-sized F1 chocolate car in the hotel lobby! I could have sworn I saw WPI licking one of the wheels. But when I yelled, "Muuummmm!" WPI insisted she didn't do anything.

Tuesday, 30 September

CHILDREN'S DAY CELEBRATION AT SCHOOL

The principal gave out goody bags to everyone today. We got boring stationery items and bookmarks. The prefect bully was up on stage with the principal. He was praised for being a good role model. Good in studies and sports. The principal said he was proud of Michael's performance as the Chief Bird leading our NDP contingent. The 3As all sniggered when he said that. I think we may have been too loud as I saw Michael shoot us an angry glance from the stage. Oh well...

A video show was also screened. A teacher had filmed all our months of rehearsals and our actual NDP performance. It felt good to watch the video, but the BEST PART was seeing Michael leading us as Chief Flapping Bird on video. Cheep, cheep, cheep!

Wednesday, 1 October

RIDING THE SINGAPORE FLYER

10am

IT'S MY BIRTHDAY TODAY! One thing good about having my birthday on Children's Day is that it's a public holiday! This year, Dad and Mum said they will bring Alvin, Anthony and I to ride on the Singapore Flyer for a treat. Anthony was really excited. He called to tell me that he has done his research on the Singapore Flyer. This is what he knows:

• The Singapore Flyer is 165 metres tall. Taller than the London Eye. Anthony's Mum said if we stack 33 giraffes on top of one another, we would reach the height of the Singapore Flyer.

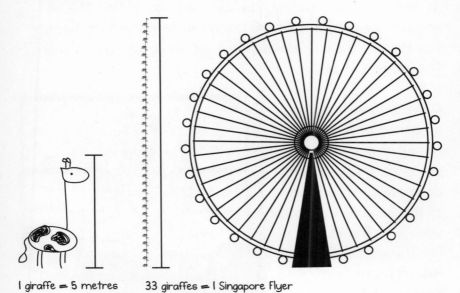

I giraffe = 5 metres   33 giraffes = 1 Singapore Flyer

- There are 28 capsules in the Singapore Flyer, with each able to carry 28 passengers.

- A ride on the Singapore Flyer takes 30 minutes.

We're ready to go. Singapore Flyer here we come!

1pm

Today must be the worst day of my life! I forgot to go to the toilet before getting into the Singapore Flyer. Imagine my panic when I realised I had to pee! Mum had a plastic bag with her. I told her I needed it as I couldn't hold my urine anymore. WPI felt sorry for me and offered to hold my plastic bag. It was terrible seeing Alvin and Anthony trying their best not to laugh at me. My baby sister was more helpful than my best friends! Sheesh...

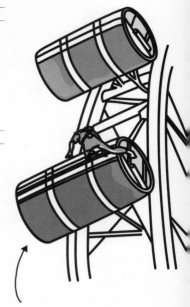

5pm

Alvin called. He apologised for laughing at me. He said he got Anthony to promise not to tell anyone what happened today.

10pm

Saw on TV that an Incredible Human Spider was scaling Suntec City! The man's name is Alain Robert and he has scaled the world's tallest buildings, like the Eiffel Tower, Petronas Twin Towers and the Empire State Building.

Ticket for my Guinness Word Records collection.

Alain, why couldn't you have climbed the world's largest observation wheel? That would have diverted everyone's attention when I had to pee in my plastic bag!

Thursday, 2 October

BOMBED IN SCHOOL

What a terrible day! When I was waiting for the school bus to send us home this afternoon, someone threw a plastic bag of urine at me from the second floor. It landed on the ground right in front of me, and I got splashed with urine! I was FURIOUS! I looked up but didn't see anyone. I tried my

best to clean myself, but it smelt awful. No one wanted to sit next to me on the bus. Not even Alvin.

Cried when I got home. Mum thought I had hurt myself. I was just angry that one of my friends had betrayed me. Why else would anyone throw a bag of urine at me? Someone must have talked about me peeing into a plastic bag at the Singapore Flyer!

Mum wanted to see the principal. I stopped her as I didn't want to blow this up. It's really embarrassing.

Friday, 3 October

Alvin swore he didn't tell anyone about me peeing in the bag. Should I believe him? Could it be Anthony?

Saturday, 4 October

BLACK AND WHITE MOVIES AT GEYLANG SERAI

Think Mum is trying to cheer me up. She said she wanted to take the whole family to check out the Hari Raya celebrations at Geylang Serai. It's part of her assignment to observe how Muslims celebrate the end of Ramadan, their fasting month. What I know of Hari Raya is that our second floor Malay neighbour has been waking up at 5am every morning recently to cook for her family before fasting starts. I really love the smell of her curry in the mornings.

Mum asked if I wanted to ask Alvin and Anthony along. I said no.

Tonight was so fun, and it helped me forget my troubles a bit. Geylang Serai was dazzling with lights and street decorations, and there were so many stalls selling all sorts of colourful things, including yummy Malay treats and sweets, like dates. Most Malays were out with their families – they were all dressed in matching outfits, cut from the same cloth!

I got totally engrossed in watching the outdoor movies at Malay Village. Watched two shows – the first was a classic Pee Ramlee movie, according to Ah Kong. The second movie was better! It was about a potty-ahnak, a Malay ghost who turns into a beautiful woman to charm young men and suck their blood! So fascinating. What I found really funny was that the potty-ahnak would always eat rojak before she killed her men. And when she floated in the air,

I could see the wire secured to her back lifting her across the movie set. Really funny.

WPI was frightened of the (potty-ahnak) but I thought she was cool with long black hair and a bloody mouth! Probably used lots of tomato ketchup.

11pm

Mum yelled at me for smearing my mouth with her lipstick. I was only trying to see what I would look like, if I had blood on my mouth. Oh man... where is her sense of adventure? WPI screamed and said I really looked like the potty-ahnak. Maybe I shouldn't try it again. I don't want to have nightmares!

Amos, it's P. Ramlee and pontianak!

Monday, 6 October

Saw Anthony in school today. He confessed. He said he talked about me peeing in the Singapore Flyer. He swore he didn't know that someone would throw a urine bomb at me. He begged for my forgiveness. This is it. We are NO LONGER friends.

EXAM FEVER

It's our final year exams next week. Po-Po has been brewing all kinds of terrible soups to help me. Mum has been pulling out all her assessment guides and "How to" books, to help me revise for my exams. I think they are both anxious because I have not talked to Anthony since Monday! As for me, I don't really care about him anymore.

Mum said if I don't do well in Mathematics this year, she'll be forced to get me tuition. I already have Mandarin tuition twice a week now. Through her research on the internet, Mum has found a mums' forum and some recommendations for a Mathematics tuition teacher. I don't wish to go for tuition four times a week. I will have no life! I promised Mum that I will study hard for my exams. I must focus! I must not think about Anthony! Or Michael! I must focus! Ah...

Wednesday, 15 October

Had two exam papers today.

Friday, 17 October

Finished two more papers. Hurray!

NO MORE EXAMS!

That's it! Exams are over. Alvin came over to play. He asked if I had talked to Anthony recently. I said no.

5pm

Anthony called to ask if we are still friends. Told him I'm still angry.

Sunday, 19 October

Ah Kong brought me to the Australian International School to watch kids playing football today. There were so many mums, dads, grandpas and grandmas watching their kids! Hmmm... Alvin reminded me yesterday that I should start raising money for Project PSP again. Maybe I could sell some local delicacies at the Australian School to earn some money. Food never fails!

Saturday, 25 October

PINEAPPLE TARTS FOR SALE

Po-Po agreed to help me bake pineapple tarts to sell at the Australian School tomorrow. She said she has an old family recipe and that her pineapple tarts had earned enough money to put

Mum through university. Hmmm... she must have sold millions of pineapple tarts through the years!

Ah Kong wrote the recipe out for me.
Looks nice pasted here!

FOR PINEAPPLE JAM
100-120g fine sugar
1 pineapple

FOR PASTRY DOUGH
500g flour, sifted
350g unsalted butter
50g fine sugar
1/2 teaspoon salt
1/2 teaspoon vanilla essence
1 teaspoon baking powder
2 egg yolks, beaten
3 tablespoons milk
1 egg, beaten, with 1 tablespoon water added for eggwash

MAKING PINEAPPLE TARTS
Grate the pineapple and cook it with its juice till almost dry. ADD sugar when cooking, stirring all the time.

Cool the jam in the fridge; it has to be firm enough to be rolled into balls.

Sift all the dry ingredients into a large bowl. ADD in the butter and rub into crumbs.

ADD vanilla essence, milk and beaten egg yolks to the crumb mixture. Knead to form a dough. Chill for at least 1/2 hour.

Prepare the pineapple jam filling by rolling it into balls.

Remove dough from fridge, roll it flat and cut into rounds. Top with balls of pineapple jam. Brush tops with eggwash.

Bake in the oven at 180 degrees C for about 15-20 minutes.

Ah Kong brought me to a football game at the Australian School. I carried my box of pineapple tarts around to show the adults. I even gave them free samples. By the end of the game, I had sold 10 containers! That's $100! Amazing.

Ah Kong said I was a good salesman. I didn't dare tell him that I said something about Dad having lost his job and that we needed money.

Amos! Please don't lie again! You can't sell food as you have no proper licence.

Sorry Mum!

10pm

My tally for Project PSP is $330 + $100 (selling pineapple tarts) = $430

Closer to reaching my objective. But I took $50 out to give Po-Po, so that's $380 left. Alvin said The Gadget, together with some software, would cost close to what I have.

Monday, 27 October

HUNT FOR MURUKKU AND A PARROT

9am

Mum has another assignment. This time, she has to review the celebration of Deepavali in Little India. That's the Festival of Lights celebrated by Hindus.

WPI and I want to buy murukku, our favourite Indian snack, made with flour and spices. Po-Po said she'd bring me to see a parrot astrologer, for the fun of having my fortune told by a bird.

It was quite crowded at the Deepavali Festival Village in Little India. There was a bazaar selling saris, flower garlands, sweets, spices and Indian artefacts. It was quite colourful and exciting. Mum said that Buffalo Road used to be filled with buffalo pens, and that the streets of Little India were full of snake charmers, fortune tellers, and even parrot astrologers. Po-Po bought some fresh prawns from Tekka Market. WPI and I bought 15 packets of murukku. We even had some prata. WPI tried a Milo Dinosaur for the first time. She loved it!

Then finally, we went to a corner of Serangoon Road where we saw an old Indian lady with her fortune-telling bird. I spent a scary 15 minutes waiting for the parrot to pick a card. I wanted to know if I had passed my Mathematics exam. The lady said I did. But the bad news was, she said I would be having tuition four times a week next year. Oh man... As for WPI, the lady said she couldn't tell what she would be getting for Christmas.

Tuesday, 28 October

BIRD BOY PICTURE

The principal talked to me this morning. He asked if I had anything to do with a picture being passed around school.

It showed a picture of Michael cut out from the school magazine, with the words "Bird Boy" written everywhere. I hadn't seen this picture before but I thought it was very well done.

I told the principal I didn't do it. I asked Alvin if he knew about the picture. He said no.

When school ended, we saw Michael as we got on our school bus. Alvin and I couldn't help ourselves – we yelled, "Cheep, cheep, cheep!" before racing onto the bus, safe from Michael who looked like he was going to eat us for lunch!

Monday, 3 November

THE SCHOOL'S BIG WALK

The whole school took part in a Big Walk today. We were part of a crowd of 20,000 people, walking at 7am in the morning. It was the principal's idea. Why do they torture poor school children like this?

The walk took us to the Marina Garage. What a strange place to keep your car. Teacher said that the Marina Garage is a dam built across the Marina Channel, which separates the sea from a freshwater lake. It's the first reservoir in the city. So why name it a garage?

Something else happened today. As we were waiting to be dismissed by our teacher, Alvin got pushed into a water pool. He wasn't hurt, but he got really wet. I asked if he saw who pushed him. He said it could be Michael, as he saw him laughing the loudest in the crowd of students. I was really angry.

Then, Alvin and I saw Anthony walk by. He soaked his face towel in the water pool and threw it at Michael. I couldn't believe it! Meek and mild Anthony, trying to help Alvin! Michael got hit in the face and was really

angry. He jumped into the water pool and started splashing water at all of us. A teacher stopped him and scolded him. Serves him right!

It's not a GARAGE, Amos! A Barrage! And really, you and your friends should just walk away from the bully!

DAM! DAM! DAM!

Are you swearing?

No Mum, just calling the barrage a dam.

Marina ~~Garage~~
(Oops, Barrage)

Alvin asked if we could be friends with Anthony again.
I agreed, since he had tried to stand up for us.

5pm

I called Anthony to say hello. He was very happy to hear
from me. I was really happy too. We have not spoken for
almost a month! It's been so long!

Anthony said that he made the bird picture of Michael
and passed it around school. Actually, I sort of guessed
that Anthony had done it. And after seeing him standing
up for Alvin, I now realise what a brave and good friend
Anthony really is. I feel lucky to have such good friends.

So, we're back to
being the 3As again!
Yippee!

Wednesday, 5 November

LAST TWO WEEKS OF SCHOOL!

The principal asked to see me this morning. At first, I
thought he was going to ask me if I was the one who
splashed water at Michael at the Marina Barrage. Instead,
he said one of our schoolmates had an accident yesterday
and needed money for an operation. The boy's parents are
out of work, so the school is trying to raise funds to help

him. The principal asked if I could lead a money collection drive. Something about me being a natural leader.

I told him I would think about it.

I told the principal I wouldn't do it as I was too busy. (Dad always says this when he doesn't want to do something.) I thought the principal looked quite disappointed. But he has many teachers who can do a better job.

We went on a bus trip to visit the accident boy at home. Alvin, Anthony and I went as we thought we could all go home early after the visit. Imagine our shock when we saw that the accident boy was the prefect bully Michael!

Michael lives in a one-room flat. He sleeps on the floor with his sister, on a thin mattress. When I saw Michael's leg, I felt quite sorry. It was in a white cast and he couldn't move. Michael was sitting on the floor, with his leg propped up on a stool.

He didn't even look at us or talk to us. His mum said he needed an operation to repair his knee cap, which had been bashed during the accident. He had been trying to save some heavy cartons of bread from falling out of a van. She told us Michael helped out at his uncle's bakery after school every day.

I felt so guilty when I heard that. Michael has to earn his pocket money from his uncle every day, the same $2 which I get from my parents, just by sticking out my hand.

When we left his house, Alvin said he had forgiven Michael for flushing his frogs down the toilet bowl and for pushing him into the water pool at the Marina Barrage. Anthony and I didn't say anything.

Monday, 10 November

I went to see the principal. I told him I would start a donation drive for Michael's operation. Anthony asked why we have to do this. My reply? "So that he will feel bad about having bullied us!" Maybe he will leave us alone after we've helped him.

Tuesday, 11 November

We started the money collection drive today. We used discarded Milo tins which the canteen operator passed us. We cut a slit at the top and sealed the lids. During recess time, we stood at the food stalls, asking for donations. Most of our friends gave 50 cents each.

Thursday, 13 November

Mum helped me to paint some new T-shirts. I brought them to school and sold all ten pieces, at $15 each. That's $150 for Michael.

Friday, 14 November

Today is the last day of school. I passed all the money we collected to the principal. He was really pleased. I reminded him to tell Michael that it was Alvin, Anthony and I who did all the hard work. He promised he would.

Saturday, 15 November

6am

I didn't sleep well last night. I could have raised more money for Michael. Looking across at WPI sleeping on her soft bed with all her stuffed toys, I felt sorry for Michael's sister. She doesn't even have a bed to sleep on.

I asked Mum to drive me to school. The principal was still around. I handed $100 of my Project PSP money over. I told him I made the money from selling T-shirts and canvas shoes in school. He said I did the right thing. The school has some funds that will be used to help Michael as well.

I've done my best. Michael and I are even now.

9pm

FOR PROJECT PSP
$380 - $100 for Michael = $280 left
(Barely enough! Still have to convince Dad to let me have it too!)

Amos, are you saving up to buy a handphone?

No Mum! Be patient, it's a secret!

Monday, 17 November

FIRST DAY OF HOLIDAYS!

Mum brought us to the Central Public Library to borrow books. We are always happy to visit the library. Mum said it's one of the best things about growing up in Singapore - having access to so many FREE books!

After lunch, we went to the No. 1 Costume shop again. Mum said she needed to rent costumes, but she wouldn't tell me what for. I found it strange that Mum rented four bumblebee suits.

Tuesday, 18 November

OH MAN! Mum wants Alvin, Anthony, WPI and I to dress up as bumblebees. It's for a charity project. Another assignment! Oh man...

Wednesday, 19 November

Anthony refused to help out. That leaves Alvin.

Thursday, 20 November

Alvin said he would dress up as a bumblebee only if I make him the leader. I agreed. Only this one time.

Saturday, 22 November

MUM THE QUEEN BEE

9am

Mum said we will be visiting a children's hospital to brighten up the place. Yeah, right. In a bumblebee suit! Thank goodness Alvin is going. We need a real clown.

4pm

Visited the hospital today as bumblebees. Alvin took the lead and was excellent! His balloons made so many children happy! WPI went around passing out packets of biscuits and sweets. I did my Durian song and the Green Hornet dance. The children had so much fun laughing,

I forgot how ridiculous I looked! Just before we left, Alvin said he saw Michael in one of the wards. I really hope he didn't see me in a silly bumblebee suit!

Saturday, 6 December

MY SISTER, THE FLOWER GIRL

Mum dragged me all the way to Changi Airport today, just to see WPI dance in a silly kindergarten school performance. So there we were, in the Butterfly Garden of the world's best airport. I was seriously trying to hide myself when WPI beamed and waved at all of us from the stage. She was a pink sausage! All of her friends too! 20 girls and boys, all in pink tutus and tights! How gross.

But really, I was amazed by all those butterflies! There were hundreds of them, all attracted by the bright pink costumes, I suppose. I found a brochure on the Butterfly Garden and read it while Mum and Dad were busy coo-ing over their pink sausage daughter. Learnt that butterflies feed on rotten pineapples. Hmm...

Amos, your sister was NOT a pink sausage! She was a pink FLOWER! Didn't you notice she had petals?

Yikes, sorry Mum! Those were petals?

Sunday, 7 December

Mum was mad with me for leaving two slices of pineapple in the balcony. I told her I was only doing an experiment. But no butterflies came. Only a trail of ants.

Monday, 8 December

There were lots of butterflies in our corridor today! They were gathered around Ah Kong's potted plants. He said he had a secret potion to lure them.

Tuesday, 9 December

I'm going to be sick. I saw Ah Kong sprinkling WPI's urine on the flowers in the potted plants. That was his secret potion to lure the butterflies!

Really, I will talk to Ah Kong to stop this immediately!

Oops! I hope I didn't get Ah Kong into trouble!

Friday, 12 December

WPI'S BIRTHDAY

We had a small family celebration for WPI's birthday tonight. Nothing big as Dad said the economy is looking bad and we need to save money. WPI's birthday cake had a picture of Alvin, WPI and

I dressed as bumblebees stuck on it! Mum called it photo-printing. I asked her what else she did with the photo. She said she used it for an article in a parenting magazine. I hope no one from school saw her article.

I refused to eat the cake. Can't bear biting into my own face.

Saturday, 13 December

Anthony called. He said his mother saw our bumblebee photo in a magazine. Oh man...

Monday, 15 December

ALVIN'S DAD

Alvin called me this morning. He sounded sad. He said his dad had lost his job. I was shocked. I wonder if Alvin has to stop school? That would be very sad. He's one of my best friends.

I told Mum about Alvin's dad. She said if there was anything that Alvin needed, maybe I could use my Project PSP money to buy it for him. Good that Mum mentioned my money. I had forgotten all about it.

Tuesday, 16 December

I called Alvin and asked if he needed money. He said he might have a problem with buying his textbooks for the new school year. But he said the school would probably give him free textbooks and uniforms. So, he doesn't need to stop school. I'm so glad he'll still be in school next year. The 3As would not be the same without him.

Wednesday, 17 December

MORE BAD NEWS

It never rains but it pours – an idiom I learnt. More bad news. Po-Po has been having a fever for the last three days. Mum is worried that it could be dengue. Mum said at Po-Po's age, it could be really serious if she caught dengue.

Ah Kong has been very worried about Po-Po. He has been looking after her, cooking porridge and sponging her with a wet cloth. WPI and I have been taking turns to sit with Po-Po. Just to accompany her as she rests, or help her take her temperature as she listens to the radio or watches TV.

Thursday, 18 December

Po-Po's fever came down this morning. Her blood test from the polyclinic came back negative for dengue. What a relief!

Friday, 19 December

Po-Po insisted on joining her friends for morning qigong at the basketball court. She must be feeling better. Ah Kong spied on her secretly from the void deck. He said, "Must make sure she doesn't faint from internal injuries."

I called Alvin again today. He said his dad would be helping some friends, working in a car wash. His mum found a family that will pay her to be a nanny. She'll be taking care of a baby.

Going to bed early. Mum said we must use less electricity to cut down on our utilities bill. That means we get to watch less TV too. So sad.

Saturday, 20 December

CHRISTMAS BAZAAR

9am

Mum agreed to let me help Alvin's dad with car washes at a Christmas bazaar.

9pm

I AM SO TIRED! Never thought it would be so hard to earn money! Guess I was lucky making money from selling T-shirts, shoes and food. Life isn't so easy for those washing cars!

The bazaar was organised by the neighbourhood Residents' Committee. There were stalls selling food like Oriental sausages, Ramly burgers, fried chicken wings and otak-otak, and other stalls selling cheap clothes, bags, VCDs, household goods and toys. Or at least, that's what Mum told me since she was the one shopping while I was slogging away washing cars. I didn't get to see much of the bazaar at all!

I spent five hours at the car wash, filling pails with water from a HDB tap, located at the foot of the block. It took seven scoops of water to fill a pail. But I only dished out five scoops each time. Strict orders from Alvin's dad. He had to pay for the use of water and was trying his best to  save whatever money he could raise from the car wash. I think I made at least 70 trips today, walking back and forth from the water point to the car park to deliver water for the car wash. I was exhausted!

 Didn't dare to complain to Alvin's dad. Didn't want him to think that I am pampered. Ah Kong said I should start helping Dad to wash his car, since I have muscles now.

Christmas Eve, 24 December

NO TOYS FOR CHRISTMAS

I peeped under the wrapper of my Christmas present, which Mum left under the tree. It was pyjamas. Oh man ... this feels like Chinese New Year all over again! Guess we won't be getting any toys. Mum has been saying that the economy is looking bleak, so we shouldn't spend so much money.

11.30pm

Dad and Mum brought us to Orchard Road for a free outdoor concert tonight. Some churches have got together to put up a performance for Christmas. It was really crowded! I think thousands of people were there, and there were songs and dances, a drama performance and a floats procession from all over the world.

I can hear Ah Kong singing Silent Night in his room.

WPI is banging on the bathroom door. She said it's almost midnight and Santa is coming.

Will tell her that Santa is not real. No way he can get through our window grills anyway, unless he wants to climb through the rubbish chute to leave her a present. I already know what she's getting. Pyjamas, what else?

DAY AT THE LIBRARY

Went to the library today. Mum proudly showed me her article with our bumblebee photo in it. I almost died! It was so embarrassing. We were called "Charity Bees". A caption read, "Siblings that volunteer together stay together!" I PROTEST! Mum did not get my permission to do this. I look ridiculous.

Just as I was leaving, I bumped into Michael and his mum. It was strange to see him on crutches, but he looked fine. He said he saw me reading magazines and wanted to say, "Hi."

I waited for him to thank me for the money I raised for his operation, but he didn't say anything. He said he saw me in the hospital a few weeks back, when he was there for his operation. I thought I heard him sniggering a bit when he said that. But he didn't say anything about seeing me in a bumblebee suit.

Tuesday, 30 December

Mum asked if I had decided what I was going to do with my PSP money. She said she already knew what it was for. Nothing escapes my mother! Yup, it's to buy the PlayStation Portable. But I won't buy one now. Not when my best friend's family is having problems with money. I can wait till things get better.

Today is the last day of the year. I can't believe one whole year has passed!

Mum asked what the high points for me this year were. Hmmm... let's see. My friendship with Alvin and Anthony! I think we have become closer this year, because we learnt to stick together and stand up to Michael. I also enjoyed trying new things, like running a stall at the car boot sale, earning money through selling things I made and being a clown - monkey, bird, pirate, wizard and bumblebee - I've done it all! Then there was the charity visit to the hospital. Felt kind of good doing something worthwhile with my time. Maybe I should try some other forms of volunteering next year. But no more dressing up as a clown!

AMOS, I AM PROUD OF YOU FOR HAVING LEARNT THE VALUE OF MONEY, IN SAVING FOR SOMETHING THAT YOU REALLY WANT!

DAD

Amos, I was really proud of you when I drove you to school that day to pass the money to the principal for Michael's operation. You did right! Happy New Year!

Hugs and kisses, Mum

Kor Kor I ♥ Luv U!
Mei Mei

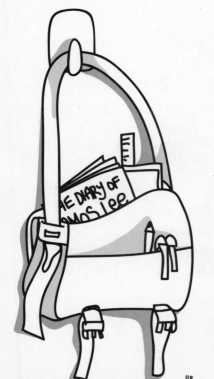

This diary will have to move to a secret location next year. No more writing in the bathroom.

amos lee

A

A380	The A380 is the world's largest passenger airliner. Manufactured by Airbus, it made its first commercial flight on 25 October 2007 from Singapore to Sydney with Singapore Airlines.
Ah Kong	Grandpa.
Ah Peh	A colloquial term for an old man.
Ang pows	Red packets that are given to children during the Chinese New Year period. The packets contain a token sum of money.

B

Bandana	A large handkerchief with patterns, worn as a band around the forehead or as a head wrap.
Batik	A traditional technique of dyeing textiles, commonly carried out in Southeast Asia.
Borders	An American bookstore chain selling a wide variety of books, CDs, DVDs and periodicals, with two branches in Singapore at Wheelock Place and Parkway Parade.

C

Char siew bao	Chinese steamed buns with pork meat filling.

F

Fried carrot cake	This is not the sweet carrot-laden dessert of Western origin. Instead, local carrot cake is made by steaming grated white radish and rice flour till a coagulated shape is achieved. This savoury "cake" is then broken into chunks and stir-fried till slightly charred. Egg, soya sauce, white pepper and chilli sauce are added too, with spring onions serving as garnish. Carrot cake can be ordered "white" or "black". The blackened version is doused generously with a thick dark sweet-salty soya sauce, while the white version contains only a sprinkling of the sauce.

H

HDB	An acronym for the Housing & Development Board, which is responsible for public housing in Singapore.

I

Ikan bilis	Anchovies.
IKEA	In Singapore, this Scandinavian furnishing store is well-known and well-loved for its affordable products as well as for its child-friendly environment, including a sizable indoor play area called Smaland, and its cafe, where Swedish and local favourites are served.

K

Kaya	Coconut egg jam.
Kinokuniya	Books Kinokuniya started as a Japanese bookstore for the Japanese community residing in Singapore in 1983. Since then, it has expanded to three branches, with its flagship store at Ngee Ann City offering an extensive collection of over 500,000 titles from all over the world.
Kopi	Hokkien for coffee.
Kueh chang	Chinese steamed glutinous rice dumplings with meat filling.

| Kueh lapis | A rich cake consisting of thin alternating layers made from sugar, butter and eggs. |

L

| Longkang fishing | Malay word for drain. Longkang fishing refers to fishing in reconstructed drains, using fishing nets and buckets. |
| Luge | A self-driving car system in which riders control the speed by pushing a pair of handlebars back and forth. At Sentosa, the Luge ride goes downhill, relying on the pull of gravity to move. After the ride, a skyride, similar to a ski lift, brings riders on chairlifts back to the starting point. |

M

Mahjong	A Chinese game played using tiles that are similar in design to dominoes. Mahjong is usually played with four persons.
Mee goreng	A dish famous in Indonesia, Malaysia and Singapore, mee goreng is made with thin yellow noodles fried with onions, chilli, vegetables, tomatoes and egg.
Milo	A popular local chocolate energy drink.

N

NTUC	The local nickname for the large local supermarket retailer, Fairprice.
Nasi lemak	A Malay dish comprising rice cooked with coconut milk, served with fried chicken, fried egg, ikan bilis (anchovies) and otak-otak (grilled spicy fish paste).
Nonya kueh	Peranakan sweet desserts. The Peranakan Chinese are descendants of Chinese traders who settled in Malacca as early as the 14th century, and later in Penang and Singapore in the 19th century. Their heritage is one of a unique, hybrid culture, with Chinese, Malay, Indian and Eurasian influences in customs, food, dressing and habits. Peranakan sweet desserts are often starch-based and multi-coloured.

O

Otak-otak	A Malay dish of spicy fish paste grilled in palm leaf.

P

P. Ramlee	A Malaysian film actor, director, singer and songwriter. Hailed as an icon in Malay entertainment for his contributions to the movie and music industry in Malaysia, Singapore and Indonesia. He passed away in 1973.
PE	Physical education class.
Pasar malam	Malay word for night street market.
Po-Po	Grandma.
Prata	An Indian bread made by stretching dough.
Pulut hitam	Black glutinous rice cooked with water, pandan leaves and sugar, served with coconut milk.

Q

Qigong	A Chinese word meaning "energy cultivation", qigong refers to a Chinese system of postures, exercises, breathing techniques and meditations that are designed to improve and enhance one's health.

R

Ramly Burger	A Malaysian burger popular in Malaysia and Singapore, with a typical serving comprising a beef or chicken patty, spread with margarine, onions, an egg, cabbage and mayonnaise, held between two buns.
Rojak	A fruit and vegetable salad dish commonly found in Malaysia, Singapore and Indonesia. It comprises bite-sized ingredients like cucumber, pineapple, turnip, bean sprouts, taupok (puffy, deep-fried tofu) and fried dough fritters, with a dressing of belacan (shrimp paste), sugar, chilli and lime juice, topped with chopped peanuts and a dash of finely chopped pink ginger buds.

S

Sambal	A spicy condiment made primarily of chilli.

Sari	The traditional dress of Indian women. An outer garment consisting a single length of cotton or silk, 5 to 7 yards long, worn with one end wrapped around the waist to form a skirt, the other draped over the shoulder. The sari is worn over a short blouse and a thin underskirt.
Satay	A popular Malay dish where small chunks of meat are marinated in spices, skewered on bamboo sticks and barbecued over an open charcoal fire.
STOMP	A web portal for Singaporeans to discuss the latest happenings in Singapore. Launched by Singapore Press Holdings, STOMP stands for Straits Times Online Mobile Print. www.stomp.com.sg.
Sushi	Cold cooked rice is dressed with vinegar, shaped into bite-sized pieces, wrapped in seaweed and topped typically with raw or cooked fish, or other seafood ingredients.

T

Teh	Hokkien for tea.
Teh tarik	A hot tea beverage with its name derived from the pouring process of "pulling" the drink to cool it.
Tekka market	A famous wet market in Singapore. A wet market is an open food market where fresh foods are displayed and sold. The floors and surroundings are usually wet as they are sprayed regularly with water to keep the environment clean.

Z

Zoe Tay	A famous top local actress who is married to a Singapore Air Force pilot.

ABOUT THE
AUTHOR

Adeline Foo lives in Singapore with her husband and
three children. She's a children's book author, with
12 published books.

The author's elder son hated reading and writing when
he was four years old. Now nine, he's written a few diaries,
which he keeps hidden from Mum. But Mum has read
every entry in his diaries (without him knowing of course),
though she has to bite her hand each time she wants to
correct his English! No, he's not called Amos, and she didn't
steal any entries from his diaries. Writing this book took
four months, and it has given the author constipation.
But some good did come out of it. The family has sworn
off eating frogs' legs, and the author has achieved the art
of multi-tasking in the bathroom, writing while doing what
most other people do in it.

If you wish to get in touch with the author, visit
www.momspanel.com.sg where Adeline blogs about the
perils of being a mum!

ABOUT THE ILLUSTRATOR

Stephanie Wong lives in Singapore and is a workaholic.

She designs and illustrates at Epigram, an independent design house and publisher of exquisitely-designed books (www.epigram.com.sg). Like Amos, Stephanie is an ardent purveyor of local cuisine and much prefers swimming to jogging. When she is not working, she can be found with her bicycle, Ralph, down by the beach or hanging out at coffee shops with friends enjoying her prata kosong (plain prata) and Teh O Peng.

To view the scribbles of the illustrator, visit www.steffatplay.blogspot.com

A NEW SCHOOL YEAR AWAITS AMOS LEE!

EXCERPTS FROM AMOS' NEXT DIARY:

...I think Mum is pregnant! She has been eating weird stuff in the middle of the night. And her stomach is getting really big! Oh man... now I have to be Big Brother to two babies!

...The 3As have decided to get into shape. We are in the swim team and Michael has joined too! We have a psycho Coach who was a former army man. He drives us nuts by barking out orders in a booming voice.

...There's a new kid in school. Her name is Somaly. She's a foreign student from Cambodia. Humph! Alvin is soooooooooooo keen to find out more about her and keeps asking me what I think of her. Not much, really. Why should I care about some girl?

Check out www.amoslee.com.sg for more updates!